TRIGONOMETRY
FOR THE PRACTICAL MAN

MATHEMATICS FOR SELF-STUDY

A GROUP OF BOOKS THAT MAKE EASY
THE HOME STUDY OF THE WORKING
PRINCIPLES OF MATHEMATICS

Arithmetic *for the Practical Man*
Algebra *for the Practical Man*
Geometry *for the Practical Man*
Trigonometry *for the Practical Man*
Calculus *for the Practical Man*

TRIGONOMETRY
FOR THE PRACTICAL MAN

J. E. THOMPSON, B.S. *in* E.E., A.M.
Professor Emeritus of Mathematics
Pratt Institute

Third Edition by

MAX PETERS
Chairman, Mathematics Department
George W. Wingate High School, New York City

AND OTHERS

D. VAN NOSTRAND COMPANY, INC.
Princeton, New Jersey

Toronto   London   Melbourne

VAN NOSTRAND REGIONAL OFFICES: *New York, Chicago, San Francisco*

D. VAN NOSTRAND COMPANY, LTD., *London*

D. VAN NOSTRAND COMPANY, (Canada), LTD., *Toronto*

D. VAN NOSTRAND AUSTRALIA PTY. LTD., *Melbourne*

Copyright © 1931, 1946, 1962, by
D. VAN NOSTRAND COMPANY, INC.

Published simultaneously in Canada by
D. VAN NOSTRAND COMPANY (Canada), LTD.

*No reproduction in any form of this book, in whole or
in part (except for brief quotation in critical articles or
reviews), may be made without written authorization
from the publisher.*

09673c25
PRINTED IN THE UNITED STATES OF AMERICA

PREFACE TO THIRD EDITION

The treatment of trigonometry used in the following pages is justified by the continued demand for this book over the years. In this new edition, however, the treatment incorporates current terminology and usage. In addition, the exercises and illustrative examples have been adapted to modern problems, although the student will continue to find numerous examples of the application of trigonometry in such fields as general measurement, surveying, and astronomy. A section of examples in analytical trigonometry has been added.

PREFACE TO FIRST
AND SECOND EDITIONS

THIS volume is one of a series giving simplified treatments of several branches of mathematics. The purpose and general plan of the series is stated in the preface to the volume on algebra. It is there stated that from the viewpoint of the classes of readers for which the series is designed, algebra may be considered as the alphabet and grammar of mathematics, the introduction to its symbolic language and the formulation of the general rules for speaking and writing it. Following algebra, geometry treats the forms and properties of figures and objects, the methods of reasoning in mathematics, and the rules of calculation and measurement of dimensions and other properties of such objects.

Continuing with this idea, trigonometry is considered as a practical and numerical application of those rules. Plane trigonometry, in particular, is treated as a useful practical subject or branch of the general subject of mathematics whose sole purpose is the calculation of the dimensions and properties of plane triangles and figures which can be thought of as made up of triangles. The chapter on angles and triangles is intended to present certain facts and rules concerning angles and triangles and their measurement from a viewpoint slightly different from that of geometry, and in a way that will lead into trigonometry and be useful in its study. The last chapter of the book is intended for those who may be interested in the beautiful relations between the trigonometric numbers or functions for their own sake or as an introduction to more advanced books on trigonometry or to the calculus.

The book has been prepared in response to a demand found by the author in his work and by the publisher in supplying books to readers and students interested in science and engineering. This demand comes from two classes of readers. One is the educated general reader who is interested in things mathematical in a general way and in particular in the uses of trigonometry in ordinary measurements, in surveying and in astronomy, which are very often referred to but frequently misunderstood and considered as abstruse and difficult. The other class of readers consists of earnest students who wish to make practical use of trigonometry in their work and also to proceed to the study of the higher branches of pure and applied mathematics, but whose preparation may not be complete and who have to study without the aid of an instructor. In either case no knowledge of mathematics beyond arithmetic and elementary algebra and geometry is required for the reading of this book.

In order to meet the needs of such readers, the range of topics and type of illustrative applications have been chosen as indicated by the table of contents. The chapter on angles and triangles has been made explicit and sufficiently complete for the purposes of the book. The more usual uses and applications of trigonometry are illustrated and described by means of a large number of fully worked out problems which are explained in detail. Finally, and perhaps most important to the readers for whom the book is designed, the method of approach and presentation of each topic and illustration is direct and natural and the language is simple, straightforward and informal, sometimes almost colloquial. The attempt has been made to secure this result without sacrifice of accuracy and clearness of statement, and figures and sketches are used wherever it has seemed that they would aid in the presentation of the material.

In this new edition the proofs of the theorems and rules of Chapter I have been omitted, and may be recalled from geometry. Several small changes have been made here and there in the text; a more detailed treatment of angle measure and its applications has been added in Chapter I, and in the last chapter the trigonometric solution of a certain algebraic equation which cannot be solved by algebraic methods has been added. Answers to many of the exercises, which were not included in the first edition, have been included in this edition, and a number of new and up-to-date problems have been added.

As in the first edition readers are again requested to send to the author or publishers notices of any errors or misprints which may be detected.

J. E. THOMPSON

Brooklyn, N. Y.
October, 1945

CONTENTS

ix

CONTENTS

INTRODUCTION

THE branch of mathematics which is called *trigonometry* is preeminently a subject devoted to measurement and numerical calculation. After the rules of counting and of handling numbers (arithmetic) are mastered, the subject of algebra deals particularly with the formulation in general symbols of the relations among numbers and the rules and methods of arithmetic. It is, so to speak, a sort of extended arithmetic, with emphasis on the forms of expression and the symbols used in writing the mathematical language. Coming next after algebra geometry develops the properties of triangles and other geometric figures and objects, and following geometry trigonometry applies the mathematical shorthand of algebra to triangles and their geometrical properties and adapts them to numerical calculation for their applications and uses in the arts, trades and sciences. Trigonometry may thus almost be called a branch of applied mathematics.

The subject of trigonometry is divided into two parts or branches, *plane* trigonometry and *spherical* trigonometry. As the names indicate these deal with planes or flat surfaces, and with the curved surfaces of spheres. Neither has anything to do with volumes or solids but only with the shapes and dimensions of figures formed in planes or on spheres. In this book we shall consider only *plane trigonometry*.

In plane trigonometry are studied the forms and dimensions of triangles and the relations between their sides and angles. If, therefore, any figure or object can be represented by means of a drawing on a flat surface in which thickness or volume is not considered, and is made up of straight lines and angles (corners), it can be treated by the methods of plane trigonometry, or simply trigonometry. By this means, with sufficient information given to work from, complete details of the shape, dimensions, angles and area of any such figure can be determined.

Since almost any problem in carpentry, machine work, land surveying and measurement, building, mechanics, astronomy, everyday observation and life, etc., can be represented by such plane figures as those just mentioned, all such problems are included in the subject of trigonometry. Thus, by means of the rules and methods of trigonometry, a few simple and easy measurements enable one to determine by calculation the shapes and dimensions of parts of machines or buildings, the shapes and areas of plots of land, the heights of mountains whose summits cannot be reached, the distances of inaccessible objects, the widths of rivers without crossing them, the size of the earth, the distances and sizes of the sun, moon and stars, the heights of the mountains on the moon, etc. In this book many problems involving such calculations are solved and the general rules and methods of solving them are fully explained.

The subject of trigonometry has an interesting history. The word "trigonometry" is derived from the Greek words for *triangle* and *measure* (τριγωνον = *trigonon* or three-angle; and μετρειν = *metrein*, to measure). The science of trigonometry was originally a branch of geometry and had for its object the measurement of triangles and their angles. It was developed by the ancient Greeks and medieval Arabs in the applications of geometry to astronomical measurement. The celebrated Greek astronomer Hipparchus of Nicaea (born about 160 B.C.) is often referred to as the founder of trigonometry; and the Egyptian Greek astronomer Ptolemy of Alexandria (died A.D. 168) applied the principles of trigonometry to stereographic and orthographic projection (used in drawing) and wrote a great work on trigonometry and astronomy which has been handed down to modern times by the Arabs, who conquered Egypt in A.D. 641, as *The Almagest.*

After the Revival of Learning in Europe during the thirteenth and fourteenth centuries trigonometry was hardly separated from the science of astronomy for several hundred years. It was finally established as a separate branch of mathematics and developed into its modern form very largely through the work of one man, the great and famous Swiss mathematician Leonhard Euler (1707–1783).

Since the calculations of trigonometry utilize some of the symbols, formulas and equations of algebra, and develop and apply the properties of triangles and related figures, it is assumed that the reader has some knowledge of simple algebra and geometry.* The first chapter recalls some of the properties of angles and triangles from geometry

---

* *Note.*—All the knowledge of algebra and geometry necessary for the study of this book may be obtained from the author's "Algebra for the Practical Man" and "Geometry for the Practical Man," published by D. Van Nostrand Company, Princeton, N. J.

and states them in a form useful in trigonometry.   The subject of angle measure and units of measure is then treated in some detail because of its fundamental importance in trigonometry, and some important applications to the measurement of the circle are given.   The reader should study this first chapter carefully and should here and throughout the book refer to an elementary book on geometry whenever it is necessary to recall or use some geometrical fact or theorem which may not be entirely familiar.

Chapter 1

ANGLES, CIRCLES AND TRIANGLES

1. Angles. The opening between two straight lines drawn from the same point is called an *angle*. Thus in Fig. 1 the two lines AB and AC from the point A form an angle. The lines are called the *sides* of the angle and the point A where they meet is called the *vertex*. The angle in Fig. 1 is referred to as "the angle at A" or as "the angle A," or by naming the ends of the lines with the letter at the vertex between the others, as "the angle BAC" or CAB. In writing either of these the symbol $\angle$ is used to replace the word "angle." Thus we write in Fig. 1 $\angle A$ or $\angle BAC$.

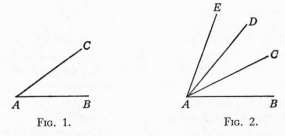

Fig. 1.   Fig. 2.

Several lines may meet at the same point as in Fig. 2. In this case it is not sufficient to name either of the angles formed by these lines by the single letter A for there are several "angles at A." Thus there are the angles BAC, BAD, BAE, CAD, CAE, DAE. In this case it is necessary and in general it is better (with certain exceptions, which we shall see later) to name an angle by means of three letters, its vertex letter and one letter on each of its sides. In Fig. 2 we should write $\angle BAC$, $\angle BAD$, etc. In naming angles by either of the methods given capital letters are to be used.

Another method of indicating and naming angles is illustrated in Fig. 3. A short curved line (part of a circle) is drawn from one side of the angle to the other, sometimes with arrow heads and sometimes without them, and a letter is placed between the sides of the angle near this curved line. In this manner the angle BAC in Fig. 3 is

1

indicated as y, $\angle BAD$ is x. This method is much used when the size of an angle is to be considered, as described below.

When two angles have the same vertex and one line between them is a side of both, the angles are said to be *adjacent*. In Fig. 2, $\angle BAC$ and $\angle DAC$ are adjacent angles.

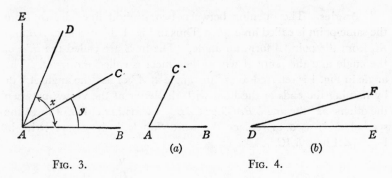

Fig. 3.   Fig. 4.

The *size* of an angle depends on and is measured by the extent of opening of its sides, and not by their lengths. In Fig. 4, $\angle BAC$ is greater than $\angle EDF$, and in Fig. 3, y is less than x. Two angles are *equal* when they may be placed so that their vertices are at the same point and the two sides of one lie along the two sides of the other, that is, the separation between their sides is the same.

Angles may be added or subtracted. The angle formed by the two outer sides of two adjacent angles is the sum of the adjacent angles. Thus, in Fig. 2, $\angle BAD$ is the sum of angles BAC and CAD. This is written $\angle BAD = \angle BAC + \angle CAD$. Similarly, $\angle BAE = \angle BAC + \angle CAD + \angle DAE$ and in Fig. 3, $y + \angle CAD = x$. From these examples it is seen at once that in Fig. 3, $\angle CAD = x - y$ is the difference between the angles x and y.

Examining these examples a little closer and writing together

$$y + \angle CAD = x$$
$$\angle CAD = x - y$$

it is seen that angles may be used in algebraic equations in the same manner as other quantities and numbers and may be added, subtracted and transposed in the same way. Thus we may write

$2x$, $3\angle ABC$, $\frac{1}{2}(\angle ABC)$, $\angle ABC \div 4$, $\dfrac{\angle ABC}{3}$, $\dfrac{y}{2}$, etc., where each of the quantities here multiplied or divided represents an angle. Each of these symbols serves to indicate the magnitude of the angle and if the angle is shown in a figure the same symbol would serve to distinguish the angle, as in the sketches referred to above.

If a line is drawn through the vertex of an angle and between its sides, it forms two adjacent angles and is said to *divide* the original angle. If the dividing line is so drawn as to make each of the two parts equal to the other it is said to *bisect* the original angle and is called a *bisecting line* or *bisector*. If two such lines are drawn so as to divide the original angle into three equal parts they *trisect* the angle. Thus, in Fig. 2, if the angles *BAC*, *CAD*, *DAE* are equal, the lines *AC* and *AD* trisect the angle *BAE*.

When one straight line meets another straight line, as *AB* meets *CD* in Fig. 5, so as to make the two adjacent angles equal, the lines are said to be *perpendicular* and each of the adjacent angles is called a *right angle*. In Fig. 5, angles *BAC* and *BAD* are right angles and *AB* is

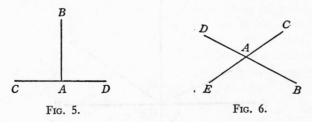

FIG. 5.   FIG. 6.

perpendicular to *CD*. This is written with the symbols $AB \perp CD$. The word "perpendicular" and its meaning must not be confused with the word "vertical." Thus, in Fig. 5, the line *AB* is *vertical* and the line *CD* is horizontal, but we can say either that *AB* is *perpendicular* to *CD* or *CD* is *perpendicular* to *AB*. A line can be vertical without being perpendicular to another line, but to be perpendicular, a line must be perpendicular *to* another. When we say "perpendicular" we must follow it by the word "to." Thus, *AB* is vertical, but *AB* is perpendicular *to CD*.

If an angle is smaller than a right angle, it is called an *acute* angle. An angle which is greater than a right angle but less than two right angles is an *obtuse* angle. When the sum of two angles is equal to a right angle they are said to be *complementary* and each is the *complement* of the other. If the sum of two angles is equal to two right angles they are called *supplementary* angles and each is the *supplement* of the other.

If the sides of an angle be extended through the vertex, as *BA* and *CA* in Fig. 6, they form three additional angles, as ∠*DAE*, ∠*DAC*, ∠*EAB*. The opposite pair of angles *BAC*, *DAE* are called *vertical angles*; angles *BAE*, *CAD* are also vertical angles. The reader will recall that it is shown in geometry that

(A) *Vertical angles are equal.*

We recall from geometry and state here two other facts concerning angles which will be found useful and important later:

(B) *If the sides of one angle are respectively parallel to the sides of another angle the two angles are either equal or supplementary.*

If both of the angles are acute or both obtuse they are equal; if one is acute and the other obtuse they are supplementary.

(C) *If the sides of one angle are respectively perpendicular to the sides of another angle the two angles are equal or supplementary.*

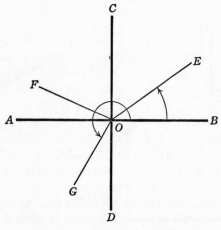

Fig. 7.

In Fig. 7, let *CD* be perpendicular to *AB* at the point *O*. Then ∠*AOC* = ∠*COB* and both are right angles. Also the vertical angles *AOD* and *COB* are equal and ∠*AOC* = ∠*BOD*. Therefore, the four angles are equal and each is a right angle.

If now we consider the angle *BOE*, we may think of the line *OE* as being drawn from the point *O* independently, or we may think of it as being *rotated* about the point *O* as center or pivot from the position

OB to the position OE, as indicated by the short curved arrow. In this case it is said that the *rotating line describes* or *generates* the angle BOE and the size or magnitude of $\angle BOE$ depends upon the *amount of rotation* of the line in passing from the position OB to the position OE. Similarly, if the rotating line moves from the position OB to OC, it is said to describe or generate the right angle BOC. If it rotates to OF, it generates the obtuse angle BOF, and at the position OA it has generated the *straight angle BOA*. Obviously a straight angle is the sum of two right angles and its sides lie in a single straight line, in this case the line AB.

Similarly, if the rotating line moves to the position OG, it is said to generate the *angle BOG*, indicated by the long curved arrow; and if the rotation continues in the same sense or direction until the rotating line is again in the position OB, it has then obviously generated a total angle which is equal to two straight angles or four right angles. Therefore, we have the important result that,

(D) *The whole angular magnitude about a point, or the sum of all the angles about a point, is equal to two straight angles.*

This result is the basis of all systems of units of angle measurement.

We define and illustrate here, referring to Figs. 8 and 9, a few other properties and relationships of angles which are used in considering the measurement of angles. In Fig. 8 AB is an object or figure of any

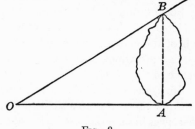

Fig. 8.

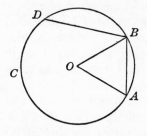

Fig. 9.

kind, the points A and B being its ends or extreme points of its outline. If O is some other point at a distance from the object, called the reference point or "point of observation," then the lines OA and OB drawn from O to the extremities of the line or object form the $\angle AOB$ and this angle is *the angle subtended at O by AB*. Thus if an observer at O sights along OA at the base of a tree or a building and again along OB at the top of the object, then OA and OB are the lines of sight, and the tree or building subtends at O the angle AOB.

In Fig. 9 C is the circumference of a circle and O is the center of the circle. The line AB, having its two ends on the circumference, is called a *chord* of the circle, and the chord and its length are denoted by the symbol $\overline{AB}$. The curved line AB, which is a part of the circle, is called an *arc* of the circle, and the arc and its length are denoted by the symbol $\overarc{AB}$.

If a radius is drawn from the center O to each of the points A and B on the circle, the two radii OA, OB form the angle AOB. This angle is called a *central angle* of the circle, and is said to be *subtended at the center* by the chord $\overline{AB}$ and also by the arc $\overarc{AB}$. The central $\angle AOB$ is said to *intercept* the chord and also the arc.

The figure AOB formed by the two radii and the arc of the circle (the "piece of pie" figure) is called a *sector* of the circle; and the small part of the sector cut off by the chord is called a *segment* of the circle. Thus the segment is what remains of the sector after the triangle AOB, formed by the radii and chord, is removed. A segment is also formed by any chord and its arc, without the radii forming a complete sector, as the segment BD.

It was discovered by the ancient Babylonians (and is proved exactly in geometry) that if the chord AB in Fig. 9 is equal in length to a radius OA of the same circle, it may be laid off as a chord, end to end, around the circle six times, the end of the sixth chord being exactly at the beginning of the first. Each of these six chords equal to the radius therefore cuts off or intercepts an arc which is equal in length to one sixth of the entire circumference of the circle.

2. Angle Measure and Units. Since the magnitude of an angle is the *difference in direction* of its sides as they proceed from a single point, the vertex, and since all possible differences in direction are included in the sum of all the angles about one point, it is natural to base the measurement of angles on the whole angular magnitude about a point. Thus, we take the whole circuit of a rotating line about one point, that is, the *circle*, as the standard of angle units, and since, as we saw in the beginning, the magnitude of an angle depends only on the direction of its sides and *not* on their lengths, the radius of the circle (length of the rotating line) is immaterial.

In the same way that the mile is not a convenient unit of length for short distances and is subdivided for convenience into rods, yards, feet, etc., so also the circle unit of angle is divided into smaller and more convenient units. Any method of division and naming of the units may be used but among all others two have been found most convenient. These are the so-called *sexagesimal* or degree system and the *circular* or radian system. These are now to be defined.

In the first system, the angle generated by the motion of the rotating radius line through one *three hundred sixtieth* part of the complete circuit is taken as the standard unit of angle and is called one *degree*. This means that if the circumference of any circle is divided into 360 equal parts and lines are drawn from the center of the circle through each point of division the angle between any two successive ones of these radial lines is one degree. For measuring very small angles, the degree is divided into 60 equal parts each of which is called one *minute* of angle. The minute is subdivided into 60 equal parts each of which is called one *second* of angle. There are thus 21,600 minutes in a circle, 3600 seconds in one degree, and 1,296,000 seconds in a circle.

The size of an angle in degrees is written as the number of unit or degree angles which it contains with a small circle just above and to the right of the last figure of the number. Thus one tenth of a circle is 36 degrees and this is written 36°, which indicates 36/360ths of the circle. Minutes are indicated as the prime or first subdivision of the degree by a single short straight mark above and to the right of the number of minutes. Thus an angle of 25 minutes is written 25′. Seconds (second subdivision of the degree) are indicated by two such marks, thus 12″. An angle whose magnitude is not a whole number of degrees is written as an ordinary mixed number (whole number and a fraction), decimal number, or in terms of the degrees, minutes and seconds which it contains. Thus $42\frac{3}{8}°$ or 42.375° is the same as 42° and $22\frac{1}{2}′$ which is written as 42° $22\frac{1}{2}′$ or 42° 22.5′ or preferably 42° 22′ 30″, which is read "42 degrees, 22 minutes, 30 seconds." This system of measuring and writing angles is used in practical calculations connected with triangles.

The system of angle measure just described gets its name from the Latin word *sexagesimus* which means *sixtieth*, from the repeated subdivision of the angle units in sixtieths. The ancient Babylonians were apparently the first to divide the circle into 360 parts, and this was because they believed that the four seasons of the year repeated themselves and the sun completed a circuit around the heavens among the stars once in 360 days, and therefore one step or grade (Latin, *gradus* = grade) or degree in one day. Thus the 360th part of the circle is a degree of angle about the center. When the Babylonians found also that the radius of a circle when used as a chord intercepts a sixth or *sextant* of the circle and therefore each sextant contains 60 degrees, or the degree is one sixtieth of the sextant, they then also divided the degree into sixty small (minute) degrees or *minutes*, the first subdivision ('), and again subdivided the minute into sixty *seconds*, the second subdivision (").

The second system of angle measurement mentioned above, the *circular* system, is also based on a subdivision of the circle, and the basic or main division is similar to the sextant but somewhat smaller than the sextant. This division is formed and defined as follows: Mark off an arc of any circle equal in length to the radius of that circle, and draw the radius from each end of the arc. The central angle formed by these two radii is called one *radian*. The radian is not divided into sixtieths like the sextant, but is divided decimally, that is, into tenths, hundredths, thousandths, etc. Any number or fraction of radians is thus written as an ordinary decimal number, as 2.58 rad., .0647 rad., 1.3276 rad., etc.

In order to get a clear idea and comparison of the several main units of angle measure (right angle or quadrant, sextant, and radian, and their subdivisions) these are described and illustrated as follows, referring to Figs. 10, 11, 12:

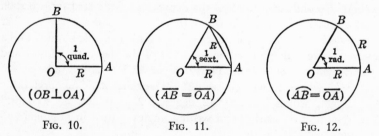

Fig. 10.   Fig. 11.   Fig. 12.

The *quadrant* of a circle is the central angle subtended by an arc equal in length to *one fourth of the circumference.*

The *sextant* is the central angle subtended by an arc equal in length to *one sixth of the circumference.*

The *radian* is the central angle subtended by an arc equal in length to the *radius* of the circle.

Stated in another manner for comparison, we can say also:

The *quadrant* is a central *right* angle.

The *sextant* is the central angle subtended by a *chord* equal to the radius.

The *radian* is the central angle subtended by an *arc* equal to the radius.

These three fundamental angle units are shown in Figs. 10, 11, 12 in a circle of any radius R.

In Fig. 10 $OB \perp OA$, and $\angle AOB$ is one quadrant.

In Fig. 11 chord $\overline{AB} = R$ and $\angle AOB$ is one sextant.

In Fig. 12 arc $\overset{\frown}{AB} = R$ and $\angle AOB$ is one radian.

We have seen already, as is evident from the names, that there are four quadrants in a circle, and six sextants in a circle. The question now arises: How many radians are there in a circle? This question is easily answered.

Thus, the circumference is proved in geometry to be equal in length to 2π times the radius, where π is the number 3.14159 . . . , that is, $C = 2\pi R$. Since there are 2π arcs equal to the radius in the entire circumference, there are 2π radians of angle about the center of the circle. In terms of degrees, therefore, 2π radians = 360 degrees, or π rad. = 180°. Dividing by the number π, therefore,

$$1 \text{ rad.} = 180°/\pi = 180 \div 3.1415926 \ldots = 57.2957795 \ldots °$$

(As the number π expressed as a decimal never comes to an end, this quotient never comes out as an exact decimal.) Expressed very closely in degrees, minutes, and seconds,

$$57.2957795° = 57° \ 17' \ 44.806''$$

or, very nearly,

$$1 \text{ rad.} = 57° \ 17' \ 45''.$$

Conversely, 1 degree = $\pi/180$ = 0.01745329 radian approximately. For approximate calculations these decimal equivalents are

$$1 \text{ rad.} = 57.3 \text{ deg.}, \quad 1 \text{ deg.} = 0.0175 \text{ rad.}$$

The complete set of relations shown in Figs. 10, 11, 12 are expressed in the following easily remembered equation:

$$1 \text{ circle} = 4 \text{ quadrants}$$
$$= 6 \text{ sextants}$$
$$= 2\pi \text{ radians,}$$

or

2 quadrants = 3 sextants = π radians = 180 degrees.

Angles expressed in degrees, minutes and seconds are called in arithmetic *compound* or *denominate numbers* and all the usual rules of arithmetic for calculating with such numbers apply to angles expressed in these units, using the table of measure given above. Calculations with angles expressed decimally in radians are performed by the usual arithmetic rules for decimals.

By means of the relations worked out above for the degree and radian systems of measure, and the table of degree measure, any angle expressed in either system of units may be easily converted to the other system. Such conversion calculations have been made and are expressed in tables. These tables are given at the end of this book. Their use is illustrated by the following two examples.

Example 1.   Convert 122° 15' to radians.

$$1 \text{ degree} = 0.0175 \text{ radians}$$
$$122° 15' = 122\tfrac{15}{60}° = 122.25°$$
The number of radians = 122.25 × 0.0175
$$= 2.139375$$
Thus,   122° 15' = 2.139375 radians

Example 2.   Convert 3.6 radians to degrees and minutes.

$$1 \text{ radian} = 57.3 \text{ degrees}$$
$$3.6 \text{ radians} = 57.3 × 3.6 = 206.28 \text{ degrees}$$
$$1 \text{ degree} = 60 \text{ minutes}$$
$$.28 \text{ degrees} = 16.8 \text{ minutes}$$
Thus,   3.6 radians = 206° 17', correct to the nearest minute.

Readers familiar with the slide rule and its use will find also that certain settings on the rule will convert angle readings in either system of units to the other, with the usual degree of precision attainable on the rule, but not with the precision to be attained by the use of the tables of conversion.

3. The Measure of Certain Important Angles.   Since, as seen at the end of article 1, a circle is equal to the sum of two straight angles, or four right angles, and a circle contains 360°, then, *a straight angle equals* 180° and *a right angle equals* 90°. If a right angle is bisected, therefore, each of the two angles formed is 45°, or one eighth of a circle, and if a right angle is trisected, each of the angles formed is 30°, or one twelfth of a circle. These three particular angles, 30, 45, 90°, with their sums and differences 15, 60, 75, are of very frequent occurrence and great importance in applied mathematics and the reader should be able to estimate and draw them very closely without the aid of instruments.

In Fig. 13, the right angle BOC is bisected by the line OD and each of the adjacent angles DOB, DOC is equal to 45°. Similarly, in Fig.

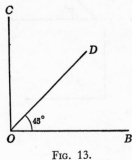

FIG. 13.

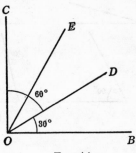

FIG. 14.

14 the right angle BOC is trisected by the lines OD and OE and each of the adjacent angles BOD, DOE, EOC equals 30°, while $\angle COD = 2(\angle BOD) = 60°$. In Fig. 15 the 30° angle COE is bisected by the line OF and $\angle COF = 15°$, while $\angle BOF = 75°$. Each of the angles of Figs. 13, 14, 15 is drawn separately in Fig. 16, and, as stated above, the reader should learn to estimate and draw them freehand. By subdivision, addition, and subtraction of these angles other angles may be easily estimated and drawn without instruments.

From the definitions given in article 1, it is seen at once that, when expressed numerically in degrees, any angle less

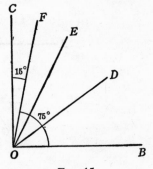

FIG. 15.

than 90° is an acute angle, while an obtuse angle is greater than 90° but less than 180°. If the sum of two angles is 90° they are complementary; thus, 60° and 30° are complementary, 75° is the complement of 15°, and 15° of 75°. Similarly, two angles whose sum is 180° are supplementary, as 147° 45′ and 32° 15′.

Since a right angle (90°) is one fourth of a circle, if two lines intersect one another at right angles, as in Fig. 17, each of the right angles *BOC, COA, AOD, DOB* is called a *quadrant* of the total angle about the point *O*, and is marked I, II, III or IV.   Any angle between 0° and

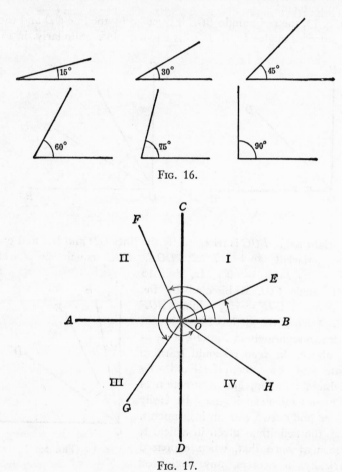

Fig. 16.

Fig. 17.

90°, as ∠*BOE*, is said to be in the *first quadrant;* any angle between 90° and 180°, as ∠*BOF*, is in the *second quadrant;* any angle between 180° and 270°, as ∠*BOG*, is in the *third quadrant;* and any angle between 270° and 360°, as ∠*BOH*, is in the *fourth quadrant.*   An angle between

360° and 450° is again in quadrant I and is equivalent to the difference between the angle as stated and 360°. Thus, 374° is in the first quadrant and is equivalent to 374° − 360° = 14°; and similarly for angles greater than 360° which lie in other quadrants.

The important angles discussed above, together with several others, which are very often used in geometry, trigonometry, drawing, and applied mathematics, are stated here in both degrees and radians, their radian measures being expressed in terms of π and also approximately as decimals.

$$360° = 2\pi = 6.2832 \text{ rad.}$$

$$270° = \frac{3\pi}{2} = 4.7124 \text{ rad.}$$

$$180° = \pi = 3.1416 \text{ rad.}$$

$$90° = \frac{\pi}{2} = 1.5708 \text{ rad.}$$

$$75° = \frac{5\pi}{12} = 1.3090 \text{ rad.}$$

$$60° = \frac{\pi}{3} = 1.0472 \text{ rad.}$$

$$45° = \frac{\pi}{4} = 0.7854 \text{ rad.}$$

$$30° = \frac{\pi}{6} = 0.5236 \text{ rad.}$$

$$15° = \frac{\pi}{12} = 0.2618 \text{ rad.}$$

$$1° = \frac{\pi}{180} = 0.0175 \text{ rad.}$$

The multiples of π in this table are derived from the relations of article 2 and the decimal values are obtained by performing the indicated multiplications and divisions of π or by use of the conversion tables at the end of the book.

4. Properties of the Circle. The general geometric properties of the circle are studied in geometry, and the value of the number π is there calculated from the relation of the radius and diameter of a circle to its circumference, the definition of π being the ratio $\pi = C/d$, where C is the length of the circumference and d is that of the diameter, both measured in the same length units.

In this article will be discussed some of the relations and calculations relating to lengths of arcs, chords, and radii, and the areas of the circle and its sectors and segments. All these will require the use of the *circular* or radian measure of central angles of the circle.

The important lines, arcs, angles, and areas of the circle are indicated in Figs. 18 and 19. Here the letter r represents the radius,

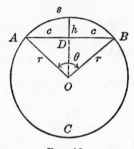

FIG. 18.

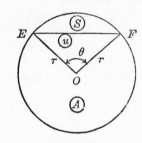

FIG. 19.

which may be of any length and measured in any unit of length. Then $C = 2\pi r$ is the length of the complete circumference, in the same unit.

In Fig. 18 the central $\angle AOB = \theta$ radians (θ is the Greek letter "theta") intercepts the chord $\overline{AB} = 2c$ length units ($\overline{AD} = \overline{BD} = c$ is the half-chord) and the arc $\overset{\frown}{AB} = s$ length units of the same kind (inches, centimeters, feet, etc.). The dotted line OD bisects the angle θ, the chord $\overline{AB}$, and the arc $\overset{\frown}{AB}$, and is perpendicular to AB at D. $\overline{OD}$ is the altitude of the triangle AOB and h is called the altitude of the segment AB or the *rise* of the arc $\overset{\frown}{AB}$.

It is recalled from geometry (see also article 5 of this chapter) that in the right triangle ODB the sum of the squares of OD and DB is equal to the square of OB; that is, $\overline{OD}^2 + c^2 = r^2$, or $\overline{OD}^2 = r^2 - c^2$, and

$$\overline{OD} = \sqrt{r^2 - c^2}. \tag{i}$$

It is also proved in geometry that the area of $\triangle AOB = \frac{1}{2}\overline{AB}\cdot\overline{OD}$; therefore

$$\text{Area } \triangle AOB = c\sqrt{r^2 - c^2}. \tag{ii}$$

Also the rise h of the arc $\overset{\frown}{AB}$ is the radius minus $\overline{OD}$, or

$$h = r - \sqrt{r^2 - c^2}. \tag{iii}$$

By transposing r in (iii) and then squaring both sides of the equation we get $h^2 - 2rh + r^2 = r^2 - c^2$, or $h^2 - 2rh = -c^2$, and by solving this last equation for c, and also for r, we find

$$c = \sqrt{h(2r - h)}, \quad r = \frac{c^2 + h^2}{2h}. \tag{iv}$$

The formulas (i), (ii), (iii) enable the altitudes of the triangle and the segment and the area of the triangle to be calculated when the radius r and the half-chord c are known; and by means of (iii) and (iv) any one of the quantities h, c, r may be found when the other two are known.

The length of the arc $\overset{\frown}{AB} = s$ can also be calculated when the radius r and the central angle θ (in radians) are known. For, the circumference is $C = 2\pi r$, and the arc s is the same part of the circumference as the $\angle\theta$ is of the total angle 2π radians about the center O. That is, as a proportion, $s : C :: \theta : 2\pi$, or $s/2\pi r = \theta/2\pi$. Multiplying this equation by $2\pi r$, $s = r\theta$. This formula states that the *intercepted arc is equal to the radius multiplied by the central angle* (in radians). From this simple and important formula any one of the three quantities r, s, θ can be found when the other two are known. Thus,

$$s = r\theta, \quad r = s/\theta, \quad \theta = s/r. \tag{v}$$

By using $r = s/\theta$ in the formulas (i)–(iv) several other useful calculating formulas may be obtained.

In Fig. 19 central $\angle EOF = \theta$ radians is the same as in Fig. 18 and chord $\overline{EF}$ the same as $\overline{AB}$. The area of the sector EOF, formed by the radii OE, OF and the arc $\overset{\frown}{EF}$ is represented by u in square units; and the area of the segment EF, formed by the chord $\overline{EF}$ and the arc $\overset{\frown}{EF}$, by S. The area of the entire circle is $A = \pi r^2$, as proved in geometry.

The area u of the sector is the same part of the circle area A as the central $\angle\theta$ is of the total angle 2π radians about the center O. That is, as a proportion, $u : A :: \theta : 2\pi$, or $u/\pi r^2 = \theta/2\pi$. Multiplying this equation by πr^2, $u = \frac{1}{2}r^2\theta$. That is, the *sector area is equal to half the product of the central angle (in radians) and the square of the radius*. From this simple and important formula any one of the three quantities u, r, θ can be found when the other two are given. Thus,

$$u = \tfrac{1}{2}r^2\theta, \quad \theta = 2u/r^2, \quad r = \sqrt{2u/\theta}. \tag{vi}$$

By using various ones of the formulas (v) and (vi) together any two of the four quantities r, s, u, θ can be found when the other two are known. For example, the first of (vi) may be written as $u = \tfrac{1}{2}r \cdot r\theta$, and by the first of (v) $r\theta = s$. Therefore

$$u = \tfrac{1}{2}rs. \tag{vii}$$

In Chapter 2 we shall define and calculate for any angle θ (in radian or degree measure) a new number called the "*sine* number of $\angle\theta$," which is represented by the symbol sin θ. We shall then find that the area of the triangle AOB or EOF in Figs. 18, 19 is equal to $\tfrac{1}{2}r^2 \cdot \sin \theta$. The area S of the segment is then equal to the area of the sector minus that of the triangle, $S = u - \triangle$. Therefore $S = \tfrac{1}{2}r^2\theta - \tfrac{1}{2}r^2 \cdot \sin \theta$, and on taking out the common factor $\tfrac{1}{2}r^2$,

$$S = \tfrac{1}{2}r^2(\theta - \sin \theta). \tag{viii}$$

This formula states that the *segment area is equal to half the square of the radius multiplied by the difference between the central angle and its sine number*, when the angle is expressed in radians.

Many interesting and important problems may be solved by the use of the formulas derived in this article. A few are solved here to illustrate the methods of use of the formulas, and others will be found at the end of this chapter for the reader to solve.

Example 3. A machine gun with an effective range of half a mile is so placed that it may be turned back and forth on its mount through an angle of 50°. How great an area does the gun command?

Solution. The area commanded is a sector of a circle, having a radius $r = \tfrac{1}{2}$ mile = 2640 feet and a central angle $\theta = 50° = .8727$ radian. By formula (vi), therefore, the area is

$$u = \tfrac{1}{2}r^2\theta = \tfrac{1}{2}(\tfrac{1}{2})^2 \times .8727 = \frac{.8727}{8} = .1091 \text{ sq. mi.,}$$

or

$$u = \tfrac{1}{2}(2640)^2 \times .8727 = \tfrac{1}{2}(6969600) \times .8727 = 3{,}041{,}184 \text{ sq. ft.}$$

Example 4. When a cylindrical tank of radius r inches lies on its side in a horizontal position and is partially filled with gasoline or other liquid, the vertical cross-section of the liquid is a segment of the circular section of the tank, the horizontal surface of the liquid being the chord of the segment and the depth of the liquid being the altitude or rise h of the segment.   The area of the segment multiplied by the length of the tank is the volume of the liquid.   This volume divided by 231 (cu. in. per gal.) is the number of gallons of the liquid in the tank.   (A numerical calculation will be given when the sine numbers of angles have been studied.)

Example 5.   A pendulum 37.46 inches long swings through such an angle that the bob swings over an arc of 3.63 inches.   Find the angle in degrees through which the pendulum swings.

Solution.   The pendulum rod is the radius $r = 37.46$ in. and the arc length is $s = 3.63$ in.   By formula (v), therefore, the angle is $\theta = 3.63/37.46 = .0960$ radian, and this, converted to degrees, gives $\theta = 5° 33' 7'' = 5.53°$.

Example 6.   The roadway of a bridge a quarter of a mile long is suspended by cables from a frame-work arch which is an arc of a circle, the horizontal roadway forming the chord of the arc (arch); and the longest supporting cable (at the center) is 100 feet long. What is the radius of the arch (arc)?

Solution.   The chord is $2c = \frac{1}{4}$ mi. $= 1320$ ft. and the half-chord is $c = 660$ ft.   The length of the center supporting cable is the altitude (rise) of the arc $h = 100$ ft.   By formula (iv), therefore, the arch is a part (arc) of a circle of radius

$$r = \frac{c^2 + h^2}{2h} = \frac{(660)^2 + (100)^2}{2 \times 100} = \frac{435600 + 10000}{200} = 2228 \text{ ft.}$$

5. Triangles.   We have already, in article 4, recalled from geometry one or two of the properties of the geometric figures called *triangles* and made use of them in certain calculations.   The reader should be also somewhat familiar with other properties of triangles as studied in arithmetic or in more detail in geometry.   The entire subject of trigonometry being founded on the properties of triangles, however, it is desirable that some of the most important and immediately useful of these be available for ready reference.   We shall therefore recall from geometry and state here without proof a few of these facts and principles.   (If the reader is not familiar with the general subject of triangles, however, he should review the necessary parts of elementary geometry.)

As indicated in the *Introduction* the name of the *triangle* is derived from the Latin word *triangulum* = three-angle, which in its turn was derived from the Greek word τριγωνον = *tri-gonon*, or three-angle.

The triangle is the familiar plane figure formed by three lines which intersect in pairs at three points. Each of these lines forms a *side* of the triangle, and each pair intersecting at a point form an angle with vertex at that point, which is also called a *vertex* of the triangle. These two intersecting lines or sides are also the sides of the angle which they form, and the angle is called an *angle of the triangle*. Thus each triangle has three (interior) angles and three sides.

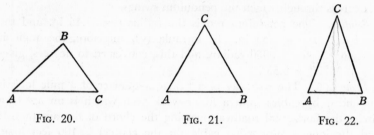

FIG. 20.   FIG. 21.   FIG. 22.

Fig. 20 represents a triangle. Here the three vertexes (or vertices) are the points *A*, *B*, *C* and the sides are *AB*, *BC*, *CA*. The figure is referred to as △*ABC* or "triangle *ABC*." The three angles of the triangle are ∠*ABC*, *BCA*, *CAB*. A triangle may have any size and shape, as determined by the lengths of its sides and the magnitudes of its angles. If the lengths of the three sides are the same, the three angles are also equal to one another and the triangle is said to be *equilateral* or *equiangular*. In Fig. 21 △*ABC* is equilateral and equiangular; side *AB* = *BC* = *CA*, and ∠*ABC* = ∠*BCA* = ∠*CAB*.

If two sides of a triangle are equal, they are called the *legs* of the triangle and it is called an *isosceles* ("equal legs") triangle. In Fig. 22, △*ABC* is isosceles and the leg *AC* = *BC*. The angle *C* opposite the third side *AB* is called the vertex. In an isosceles triangle, the angles between each leg and the third side are equal. In Fig. 22, ∠*CAB* = ∠*CBA*. An equilateral triangle is also isosceles since any two of its sides are equal. When no two of the sides of a triangle are equal the triangle is called a *scalene* triangle. In Fig. 20 △*ABC* is scalene.

If one of the angles of a triangle is a right angle, the triangle is called a right-angled triangle, or more generally a *right triangle*. In Fig. 23, △*ABC* is a right triangle, the angle at *C* being the right angle. The two sides of the triangle which are perpendicular to one another, are called the *legs* of the right triangle, and the other side, which is opposite the right angle, is called the *hypotenuse*. In Fig. 23, $\angle ACB$ is frequently called $\angle C$ and is the right angle, AC and BC are the legs, and AB is the hypotenuse.

The angles A and B of the right $\triangle ABC$, Fig. 23, are called the *acute angles* of the right triangle (the reason will appear later), BC is the *side opposite $\angle A$*, and AC is the *side adjacent to $\angle A$*. Similarly, AC is the side opposite $\angle B$, and BC the side adjacent to $\angle B$.

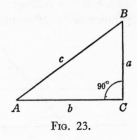

Fig. 23.

The letters A, B, C may be used simply to denote the angles *at* the points A, B, C, since there is only one interior angle at each vertex, or they may be used as algebraic symbols to indicate the angles themselves and their magnitudes. Thus $C = 90°$, $A = 30°$, etc.

The sides may be denoted as above by AB, BC, CA or more conveniently by the small letters a, b, c, which serve simply to designate the sides and also as algebraic symbols to represent their length, as $a = 6$ inches, $c = 12$ inches, etc. In every case when small letters are so used and the angles are indicated by capital letters at the vertices, the side *opposite* any angle is indicated by the *same* (small) letter as that used for the angle. This is shown in Fig. 23 where side a is opposite $\angle A$, b is opposite $\angle B$ and c opposite $\angle C$, and also in Fig. 24, which is not a right triangle.

A triangle which has no right angle is called an *oblique triangle*, from the fact that any two intersecting lines which are not perpendicular to one another are said to be oblique. When one of its angles is an obtuse angle, a triangle is said to be an *obtuse* triangle. If all the angles of a triangle are acute it is called an *acute* triangle. Figs. 24 and 25 are oblique triangles. That of Fig. 24 is acute and Fig. 25 is obtuse.

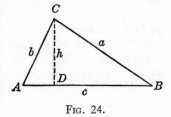

Fig. 24.

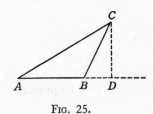

Fig. 25.

The side of a triangle on which it is supposed to stand is called the *base;* in Fig. 20 or Fig. 21, AB is the base. The third, or unequal side of an isosceles triangle, is called its base no matter on which side it stands. Thus, in Fig. 22, AB is the base. A straight line drawn perpendicular to the base and through the opposite vertex is called the *altitude* of the triangle. Thus, in Fig. 20, a line through C and perpendicular to AB would be the altitude of the triangle ABC. In the

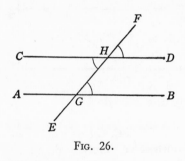

Fig. 26.

acute and in the obtuse triangles of Figs. 24, 25, AB is the base and CD the altitude in each case. In the right triangle of Fig. 23, a is the altitude and b is the base.

There is one property of triangles which is so extremely important that we give a proof of it, even though it is already proved in geometry. For use in the proof, and also for later use, we first recall and state some further angle definitions, referring to Fig. 26.

If two straight lines are drawn in the same direction, the angle between them is zero and the lines are said to be *parallel* to one another, and are called *parallels.* In Fig. 26, AB is parallel to CD. This is written $AB\|CD$. If a third straight line, such as EF in Fig. 26, intersects the two parallels, as at G and H, it is called a *transversal.* The angles CHE and BGF, or the angles DHE and AGF, are called *alternate interior angles* of the parallels. Angles BGF and DHF, and each of the other similarly situated and related pairs of angles, are called *interior-exterior angles* or *corresponding angles* of the parallels. Angles BGF and DHE, or AGF and CHE, are *interior angles;* and angles CHE and BGF or angles AGF and DHE are alternate interior angles of the parallels.

From these definitions and previously proved results pertaining to angles and parallels the following fundamental facts are proved in geometry:

(E) *Corresponding angles of parallels, formed by a transversal, are equal.*

(F) *Alternate interior angles of parallels, formed by a transversal, are equal.*

(G) *Interior angles of parallels, formed by a transversal, are supplementary.*

By using these results the important triangle property referred to above can now be proved.

In Fig. 27, let the line DE be drawn through the vertex C of $\triangle ABC$ and parallel to the side AB, and let ABC represent any triangle whatever. Then, AB and DE are
parallels, and AC, BC are transversals. Let C represent the original $\triangle ACB$. Then, according to the results obtained above, the alternate interior angles B and BCE are equal; also, angles A and ACD are equal. Furthermore, the sum of the angles

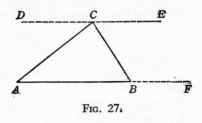

FIG. 27.

ACD, ACB, BCE is 180°, since they form the straight angle DCE. That is,

$$\angle ACD + \angle BCE + C = 180°.$$

But, as we have just seen that $\angle ACD = A$ and $\angle BCE = B$, this means

$$A + B + C = 180°.$$

We thus have the extremely important result that

(H) *The sum of the angles of a triangle equals 180° or π radians.*

This is true of any and all triangles, and is one of the very foundations of trigonometry.

In the case of the equilateral (equiangular) triangle, the three angles are equal and, therefore, each is one third of the total 180°, of their sum. Therefore,

(J) *Each angle of an equilateral triangle equals 60° or one sextant.*

From the result (H) we can obtain another which will be of use to us later. If one side of a triangle be extended beyond the vertex as at BF, Fig. 27, the new angle formed is called an *exterior angle* of the triangle. Thus, in Fig. 27, $\angle CBF$ is an exterior angle of $\triangle ABC$. Similarly, exterior angles could be formed by extending BC and CA. The interior angle B is called the interior angle adjacent to the exterior $\angle CBF$, and angles A and C are called the *opposite interior angles*. It is at once seen that the exterior angle and its adjacent interior angle are supplementary. We now proceed to show the relation between the exterior and its opposite interior angles.

We have just found that in the $\triangle ABC$, $A + B + C = 180°$.

$$\therefore \quad A + C = 180° - B.$$

Also, since B and $\angle CBF$ are supplementary,

$$\angle CBF = 180° - B.$$

Comparing these two equations we see that

$$\angle CBF = A + C,$$

that is,

(K) *An exterior angle of a triangle equals the sum of the opposite interior angles.*

In arithmetic the reader first discovered, and in geometry found it strictly proved, the familiar fact that the area of any rectangle or parallelogram is equal to the product of its base (length) and its altitude (height). As any triangle is half of some parallelogram, formed by drawing a diagonal (line joining opposite vertexes) it follows at once that

(L) *The area of any triangle equals half the product of its base and altitude.*

We have already made use of this fact but it is stated here for record and reference. Another important property of triangles of any shape is proved by drawing a line parallel to one of its sides and cutting across the other two as a transversal. Then it is proved in geometry that

(M) *A line parallel to one side of a triangle divides the other two sides into two segments each whose lengths are proportional.*

Refer to Fig. 20 and suppose a line drawn parallel to the side AC and cutting across the other two sides, meeting side AB at a point P and BC at a point Q. The fact just stated, applied to this triangle, states that as a proportion $AB : AP = CB : CQ$. In the form of an equation this proportion becomes

$$\frac{\overline{AB}}{\overline{AP}} = \frac{\overline{CB}}{\overline{CQ}} \tag{1}$$

For the purposes and uses of trigonometry right triangles (having one right angle) are among the most important of all triangles. We now apply some of the results stated or proved in this section to right triangles, and discuss some of their properties which will be especially important in the next chapter.

Since by (H) above, the sum of the angles of any triangle is 180° and a right triangle has one 90° angle, the sum of the other two angles of a right triangle is 90°. Therefore, they must each be less than 90°, that is, each is an acute angle.   A right triangle has, then, one right angle and two acute angles, and since the sum of these two is 90°,

(N) *The acute angles of a right triangle are complementary.*

For this reason, the acute angles of a right triangle are sometimes called *co-angles*.   Thus, if one acute angle of a right triangle is 15° the other is 75°, if one is 30° the other is 60°, and if one is 45° the other is 45°.

Since the area of any triangle is half the product of its base and altitude and when a right triangle stands on one of its legs as base the other is the altitude, as in Fig. 23, we have this rule for any right triangle:

(P) *The area of a right triangle is half the product of its legs.*

If, in the right $\triangle ABC$ of Fig. 28 below, the line DE is drawn parallel to BC, then by equation (1) above we have

$$\frac{\overline{AC}}{\overline{AE}} = \frac{\overline{AB}}{\overline{AD}},$$

or, denoting the sides of $\triangle ABC$ by a, b, c and the corresponding sides of $\triangle ADE$ by a', b', c', this proportion may be written as

$$\frac{b}{b'} = \frac{c}{c'}. \tag{2}$$

Similarly, if we draw $DF \| AC$, then $FC = DE = a'$ and we have the proportion $\overline{AB}/\overline{AD} = \overline{CB}/\overline{CF}$, or

$$\frac{c}{c'} = \frac{a}{a'}. \tag{3}$$

By comparing the equations (2) and (3) it is seen that the ratios b/b' and a/a' are equal to the same quantity, c/c',

$$\therefore \quad \frac{a}{a'} = \frac{b}{b'}. \tag{4}$$

By transforming the proportion (3), algebraically, we get

$$\frac{a}{c} = \frac{a'}{c'}.$$

Similarly from (2),

$$\frac{b}{c} = \frac{b'}{c'}, \left.\begin{array}{c}\\ \\ \\ \end{array}\right\} \tag{5}$$

and from (4),

$$\frac{a}{b} = \frac{a'}{b'}.$$

In Fig. 28 since DE‖BC, ∠ADE = ∠ABC. Also, A is the same angle in both triangles ABC, ADE. Therefore, the acute angles of

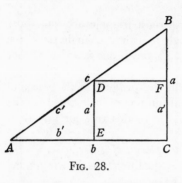

FIG. 28.

△ADE are the same as those of △ABC. These two triangles are drawn separately in Fig. 29. Thus, in Fig. 29 the triangles ADE and ABC have the *same angles but different sides*. Even though the sides are different, the proportions (5) show that the *ratio* of side a to side c is the same for △ABC as for △ADE. The ratio of b to c is also the same for both triangles, and similarly for the ratio of a to b.

We did not specify any particular lengths for the sides of △ABC or △ADE; only the angles are the same. They may, therefore, be any two right triangles *with equal angles*, regardless of the lengths of the sides. We have, then, the extremely important result that

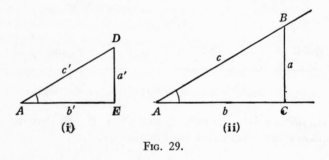

FIG. 29.

(Q) *The ratios of corresponding sides are the same for all right triangles with equal acute angles.*

This is the most used property of right triangles in all trigonometry.

There is one other property of right triangles which is of equal importance. This principle is proved in geometry, and indeed we have already referred to it and used it in this chapter. Because of the need for complete familiarity with this fact we give here a proof of it which is somewhat simpler than that usually given in elementary geometry.

In Fig. 30 the triangle ABC is a right triangle with right angle at C, and with hypotenuse c and legs a, b. Using the hypotenuse c as side, draw the square $ABDE$. Then draw $DF \perp AC$, $EG \perp DF$, and extend BC to meet EG at H. Then, $AC \| EG$ since both are perpendicular to DF and in the same direction, and $BH \| DF$. Therefore, by (B), article 1, $\angle ADF = \angle EBH$ and $\angle DEG = \angle BAC$. But, $\angle EBH = 90° - \angle ABC$ $= \angle BAC$. The acute angles and hypotenuses of the four right triangles ABC, BEH, EDG, DAF are, therefore, equal and hence the triangles are all equal. Therefore, the corresponding sides $AF = DG = EH$ $= BC = a$ and $DF = EG = BH =$

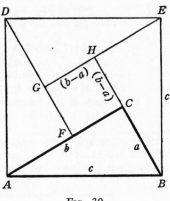

Fig. 30.

$AC = b$, and hence the sides of the small square $CH = HG = GF = FC = \overline{AC} - \overline{AF} = b - a$.

Now, the area of each of the right triangles is $\frac{1}{2}ab$ and that of the little square $CFGH$ is the square of the side, that is, $(b - a)^2$. The sum of the areas of the little square and the four triangles is $(b - a)^2 + 4(\frac{1}{2}ab)$ or $(b - a)^2 + 2ab$. But, this total area is the area of the large square $ABDE$ of side c, which is c^2. We have, therefore,

$$c^2 = (b - a)^2 + 2ab,$$

or,

$$c^2 = b^2 - 2ab + a^2 + 2ab.$$

$$\therefore \quad c^2 = a^2 + b^2. \tag{5a}$$

Since $\triangle ABC$ represents *any* right triangle this equation states that

(R) *The square of the hypotenuse of a right triangle equals the sum of the squares of its legs.*

This result constitutes another extremely important and useful property of the right triangle. It is called the law or *Theorem of Pythagoras*, after the ancient Greek who first proved it. The proof we have given above was first given by a mathematician of India named Bhaskara, who was born in the year 1114.

6. Exercises and Problems.

1. Find the sum and also the difference of the following two angles: 28° 17′, 59° 27′.

2. Find the sum and the difference of 87° 46′, 49° 28′.

3. Multiply and also divide each of the following two angles by 3: 45° 36′, 91° 24′.

4. Given $A = 117° 48'$, $B = 23° 26'$. Find $\frac{1}{2}(A + B)$ and $\frac{1}{2}(A - B)$.

5. Convert each of the following angles into radians: 47°, 18° 30′, 125° 48′.

6. Express each of the following numbers of radians in sexagesimal measure, to the nearest whole minute: 1.6, 2.4, $\frac{2}{3}\pi$, $.85\pi$.

7. Draw each of the following angles by making use of article 3, and express each in radians, both in terms of π and as decimals: 105°, 120°, 135°, 150°.

In Exercises 8–19 r represents the radius of a circle, θ is a central angle, s the intercepted arc, and u the sector area. In each case find the two quantities not given, naming the unit in which each is expressed.

Ex.	r	θ	s	u
8.	10 in.	2 rad.		
9.	40 cm.		30 cm.	
10.	3 ft.			36 sq. ft.
11.		25° 9′	3.5 in.	
12.		3 rad.		10 sq. ft.
13.			9.5 cm.	42.4 sq. cm.
14.	565 in.	30 deg.		
15.	210 rods		319 rods	
16.	7.05 ft.			100 sq. ft.
17.		1.8 rad.	2.6 yd.	
18.		38° 18′		28.3 sq. m.
19.			18.4 in.	83.2 sq. in.

20. The tank of Example 4, article 4, has a radius of 3 ft. and the gasoline in it is 18 in. deep at the deepest point. How wide is the surface of the liquid from side to side of the tank?

21. A cow is tethered to a stake so placed that she grazes over a sector of 65 degrees, and the greatest distance she can walk at the end of the taut rope is 50 feet. How long is the rope, and over what area does she graze?

22. What is the length of the curved front line which the machine gun of Example 3, article 4, commands?

23. The radius of the earth is about 4000 miles, and two cities are so located that the straight line distance from one to the other through the earth is 2000 miles. If it were possible to drive a straight tunnel joining the cities, how far below the surface would the tunnel be at its center?

24. Two angles of a triangle are $A = 23° 47'$ and $B = 54° 18'$. What is the third angle C?

25. If a line is drawn on the face of a watch from the point on the hour and minute circle marking 12:00 o'clock to the point marking 4:24 o'clock, what are the angles of the triangle formed by this line and the radii to the two points? Express each angle in both sexagesimal and circular measure.

Chapter 2

RIGHT TRIANGLES
AND ANGLE FUNCTIONS

7. The Right Triangle Ratios.   Angle Functions.   We have seen in article 5 that so long as the acute angles of a right triangle remain unchanged, the ratios of pairs of its sides also remain unchanged regardless of the lengths of its sides.   In Fig. 31 let $\angle A = 30°$ (then by (N), article 5, $B = 60°$) and let the angles and corresponding opposite sides be represented by A, B, C and a, b, c.   In Fig. 32 the angles

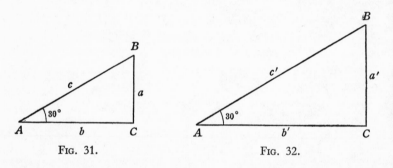

Fig. 31.   Fig. 32.

A, B, C are the same as in Fig. 31: $A = 30°$, $B = 60°$ (of course $C = 90°$), but the sides are different.   Let these be a', b', c'.

According to the first one of the equations (5), however, even though a', b', c' are not equal to a, b, c, the quotient a/c obtained by dividing the length a by the length c will be the same as the quotient a'/c' obtained by dividing the length a' by the length c'.   Similarly, if another right triangle, larger or smaller, but with the *same acute angles*, be drawn and the corresponding sides measured it will be found that the *same quotients* will be obtained, because Figs. 31 and 32 represent *any* triangles with the same angles.   In the same way, the quotients or ratios b/c and a/b remain the same for the *same angle* in a right triangle of any size.

The reader should make careful drawings of right triangles with the same angles but different sides and test these results by actual measurements of the sides and calculation of the ratios. If the angles are really equal and the measurements are accurately made, it will be found that the above results are verified. The measurements and calculations should be repeated with different angles. It will then be found that the quotients are not the same as for the first angle.

We thus find that the values of the right triangle ratios depend *only on the angles* and that to each different angle there corresponds a different set of these values. Any number or quantity which is related in this way to another number or quantity is called a *function* of that second number or quantity. Therefore, *the right triangle ratios are functions of the acute angles of the triangle.* These ratios or numbers are, therefore, characteristic numbers associated with and belonging to the angles. They are of the greatest importance and usefulness in the study of angles and triangles (trigonometry) and are given special names.

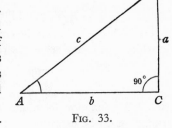

Fig. 33.

In Fig. 33, the ratio or number obtained by dividing the length *a* by the length *c*, that is, $a \div c$, is called the *sine* of the angle *A*. The ratio or number $b \div c$ is called the *cosine* of the angle *A*. The number $a \div b$ is called the *tangent* of the angle *A*. Writing these out together,

$$a \div c = \text{sine of } \angle A,$$
$$b \div c = \text{cosine of } \angle A,$$
$$a \div b = \text{tangent of } \angle A.$$

The expression "sine of $\angle A$" is abbreviated and written *sin A*, which is read "sine *A*." The expression "cosine of $\angle A$" is written *cos A*, which is read "cosine *A*," and "tangent of $\angle A$" is written *tan A*, which is read "tangent *A*." In this abbreviated form then we have for any right triangle with right angle *C* and acute angles *A*, *B* and with corresponding opposite legs *a*, *b* and hypotenuse *c*:

$$\sin A = \frac{a}{c}, \quad \cos A = \frac{b}{c}, \quad \tan A = \frac{a}{b}. \tag{6}$$

These three formulas are the *fundamental formulas* of the right triangle and should be thoroughly understood and committed to memory. In trigonometry it is necessary to use them constantly and it must not be necessary to refer to the printed page or to notes in order to recall and use them.

A convenient way to remember the formulas is to note that in Fig. 33, a is the leg *opposite* angle A, and c is the *hypotenuse* of the right triangle. We can write, therefore, for either acute angle of any right triangle, whether marked with the same letters as in Fig. 33 or not:

$$\text{sine} = (\text{opposite leg}) \div (\text{hypotenuse}).$$

Similarly, in Fig. 33 side b is the leg *adjacent* to angle A and we have:

$$\text{cosine} = (\text{adjacent leg}) \div (\text{hypotenuse}),$$

and

$$\text{tangent} = (\text{opposite leg}) \div (\text{adjacent leg}).$$

These three forms may be conveniently abbreviated to the following, in which form they are easily remembered:

$$\sin = \frac{\text{opp}}{\text{hyp}}, \quad \cos = \frac{\text{adj}}{\text{hyp}}, \quad \tan = \frac{\text{opp}}{\text{adj}}. \tag{7}$$

In all the function formulas, the dimensions of all the sides of the triangle must be expressed in the same unit of measurement.

Using the last form for writing the angle functions, it is seen at once that in Fig. 33 the functions of the acute angle B are:

$$\sin B = \frac{b}{c}, \quad \cos B = \frac{a}{c}, \quad \tan B = \frac{b}{a}. \tag{8}$$

Comparing these formulas with formulas (6) it is seen at once that the sine of $\angle B$ is the same as the cosine of $\angle A$. Now, A and B are complementary angles, as we have seen in article 5, that is, B is the co-angle of A. It is for this reason that b/c, which is the sine of B, is called the *co*-sine of A.

In the same way the ratio b/a which is the tangent of B is called the *co*-tangent of A, and a/b which is the tangent of A is the cotangent of B. This new function is written *cot A* and read "cotangent A," or *cot B*, which is read "cotangent B." We thus have, in Fig. 33,

$$b \div a = \text{cotangent of } \angle A,$$

$$a \div b = \text{cotangent of } \angle B,$$

or in the abbreviated form of formulas (6) and (8),

$$\cot A = \frac{b}{a}. \tag{6a}$$

$$\cot B = \frac{a}{b}. \tag{8a}$$

These formulas may be added to those of (6) and (8) for the corresponding angles.   In the easily remembered form corresponding to (7) we can write

$$\cot = \frac{\text{adj}}{\text{opp}}, \tag{7a}$$

which forms a part of the list of (7).

Of the four angle functions or numbers, sine, cosine, tangent, cotangent, the last is not so much used as the first three, these three being of constant use in all triangle calculations.

Besides these four functions there are two others which are sometimes used for special purposes. We shall have very little need for them in this book, but for the sake of completeness we give them here. They are called the *secant* and the *cosecant* and are written *sec, csc*. Referring to the right triangle of Fig. 33 they are defined as follows:

Similarly,

$$\left.\begin{array}{ll} \sec A = \dfrac{c}{b}, & \csc A = \dfrac{c}{a}. \\[2mm] \sec B = \dfrac{c}{a}, & \csc B = \dfrac{c}{b}. \end{array}\right\} \tag{9}$$

It is seen from these that in general

$$\sec = \frac{\text{hyp}}{\text{adj}}, \quad \csc = \frac{\text{hyp}}{\text{opp}}. \tag{10}$$

Because of their fundamental importance in trigonometry the angle functions or numbers are also called *trigonometric functions*. For convenient reference, the complete list is tabulated below in Table I. At the end of this chapter the numerical values of the functions are calculated for a number of triangles and angles. In the next article we develop a few important algebraic relations which exist among the several functions.

TABLE I

General		
$\sin = \dfrac{\text{opp}}{\text{hyp}}$	$\sin A = \dfrac{a}{c}$	$\sin B = \dfrac{b}{c}$
$\cos = \dfrac{\text{adj}}{\text{hyp}}$	$\cos A = \dfrac{b}{c}$	$\cos B = \dfrac{a}{c}$
$\tan = \dfrac{\text{opp}}{\text{adj}}$	$\tan A = \dfrac{a}{b}$	$\tan B = \dfrac{b}{a}$
$\cot = \dfrac{\text{adj}}{\text{opp}}$	$\cot A = \dfrac{b}{a}$	$\cot B = \dfrac{a}{b}$
$\sec = \dfrac{\text{hyp}}{\text{adj}}$	$\sec A = \dfrac{c}{b}$	$\sec B = \dfrac{c}{a}$
$\csc = \dfrac{\text{hyp}}{\text{opp}}$	$\csc A = \dfrac{c}{a}$	$\csc B = \dfrac{c}{b}$

8. Some Relations among the Functions of an Angle.   Since, in Table I, $\sin A = a/c$ and $\cos A = b/c$, we get by dividing the sine by the cosine algebraically,

$$\frac{\sin A}{\cos A} = \frac{\left(\dfrac{a}{c}\right)}{\left(\dfrac{b}{c}\right)} = \frac{a}{c} \cdot \frac{c}{b} = \frac{a}{b}.$$

But $a/b = \tan A$, therefore,

$$\frac{\sin A}{\cos A} = \tan A.$$

Similarly, we would find $\sin B/\cos B = \tan B$, or for *any* angle

$$\frac{\sin x}{\cos x} = \tan x \tag{11}$$

In Table I we have also $\tan A = a/b = 1/\left(\dfrac{b}{a}\right) = 1/\cot A$. Similarly, $\tan B = 1/\cot B$ and in general for any angle x,

$$\tan x = \frac{1}{\cot x}, \quad \therefore \quad \cot x = \frac{1}{\tan x} \cdot \tag{12}$$

Using this result with (11) we get

$$\cot x = \frac{1}{\tan x} = \frac{1}{\dfrac{\sin x}{\cos x}} = \frac{\cos x}{\sin x} \cdot$$

For any angle, therefore,

$$\cot x = \frac{\cos x}{\sin x} \cdot \tag{13}$$

We have, also, in Table I, $\sec A = c/b = 1/\left(\dfrac{b}{c}\right) = 1/\cos A$, and the same for B. Similarly, $\csc A = c/a = 1/\left(\dfrac{a}{c}\right) = 1/\sin A$, and the same for B. In general, therefore, for any angle,

$$\left.\begin{array}{l} \sec x = \dfrac{1}{\cos x}, \quad \csc x = \dfrac{1}{\sin x}; \\[2mm] \therefore \quad \cos x = \dfrac{1}{\sec x}, \quad \sin x = \dfrac{1}{\csc x} \cdot \end{array}\right\} \tag{14}$$

Since the angle functions are ordinary numbers obtained by dividing lengths of lines by one another, the same operations may be performed with them as with other numbers. The above transformations involving division illustrate this statement. Similarly, $\sin A$ may be squared when its value is known. In symbols this means, algebraically,

$$(\sin A) \cdot (\sin A) = (\sin A)^2.$$

This does not mean that the angle A is squared, it is the *sine* number corresponding to the angle A which is squared. In order to indicate this more clearly and simply, it is written *sin² A*, which means the *square of the sine of A* and is read "sine square A." Similarly, *cos² A* means the *square of the cosine of A* and is read "cosine square A," and likewise for any function of any angle.

Now, in any right triangle with legs a, b and hypotenuse c, according to equation (5a) in article 5,

$$a^2 + b^2 = c^2.$$

Dividing this equation by c^2 we get

$$\frac{a^2}{c^2} + \frac{b^2}{c^2} = 1,$$

or

$$\left(\frac{a}{c}\right)^2 + \left(\frac{b}{c}\right)^2 = 1.$$

But, in such a triangle $a/c = \sin A$ and $b/c = \cos A$. Therefore,

$$\sin^2 A + \cos^2 A = 1. \tag{15}$$

Similarly, we would find that $\sin^2 B + \cos^2 B = 1$, and, in general for any angle,

$$\sin^2 x + \cos^2 x = 1. \tag{16}$$

We thus have the remarkable result that if we square the sine and also the cosine of any angle and add the results the sum is always equal to 1.

All the relations developed in this article refer to functions of one and the same angle and no two different angles can be used in any one formula at the same time. Thus, we cannot say that $\sin A/\cos B$ equals $\tan A$ or $\tan B$, nor that $\sin^2 x + \cos^2 y$ equals 1, but only for any one angle x, $\sin x/\cos x = \tan x$, $\sin^2 x + \cos^2 x = 1$, etc.

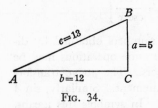

Fig. 34.

9. Calculation of Functions of Angles of Right Triangles. Let us calculate the angle numbers or functions of each of the acute angles of a right triangle whose legs are 5 inches and 12 inches and whose hypotenuse is 13 inches. If we represent the triangle by Fig. 34, we have $a = 5$, $b = 12$, $c = 13$. Then $C = 90°$ and the functions of A and B are found by using the function formulas.

Carrying the computations to only three decimal places we have:

$$\sin A = \frac{a}{c} = \frac{5}{13} = .385,$$

$$\cos A = \frac{b}{c} = \frac{12}{13} = .923,$$

$$\tan A = \frac{a}{b} = \frac{5}{12} = .417,$$

$$\cot A = \frac{b}{a} = \frac{12}{5} = 2.400,$$

$$\sec A = \frac{c}{b} = \frac{13}{12} = 1.083,$$

$$\csc A = \frac{c}{a} = \frac{13}{5} = 2.600.$$

After finding $\sin A = .385$ and $\cos A = .923$ we could, of course, use the relations given in the formulas (11)–(14) of the last article and calculate the tangent, cotangent, secant and cosecant as follows:

$$\tan A = \frac{\sin A}{\cos A} = \frac{.385}{.923} = .417,$$

$$\cot A = \frac{1}{\tan A} = \frac{1}{.417} = 2.400,$$

or

$$\cot A = \frac{\cos A}{\sin A} = \frac{.923}{.385} = 2.400,$$

and

$$\sec A = \frac{1}{\cos A} = \frac{1}{.923} = 1.083,$$

$$\csc A = \frac{1}{\sin A} = \frac{1}{.385} = 2.600.$$

In the actual calculation of the functions of all angles this is the method used, the sine and cosine being calculated by certain special methods. For the study of triangles, however, and in order to familiarize the beginning student with the relations of the functions to the triangle, it is better to calculate the functions directly from the triangle than by the use of the relations among the functions. After the functions are found by direct calculation, however, these relations may be used as checks on the calculations.

In finding the functions of the angle B in the right triangle of Fig. 34 we can make use of the complementary relation between A and B and their functions and simply write out the functions and co-functions of B by inspection of the corresponding respective co-functions and functions of A as already found. This will be a useful and interesting exercise for the reader, but we shall here calculate all the functions of B directly from the triangle.

$$\sin B = \frac{b}{c} = \frac{12}{13} = .923,$$

$$\cos B = \frac{a}{c} = \frac{5}{13} = .385,$$

$$\tan B = \frac{b}{a} = \frac{12}{5} = 2.400,$$

$$\cot B = \frac{a}{b} = \frac{5}{12} = .417,$$

$$\sec B = \frac{c}{a} = \frac{13}{5} = 2.600,$$

$$\csc B = \frac{c}{b} = \frac{13}{12} = 1.083,$$

In each of the fractions giving the twelve functions of A and B both numerator and denominator are expressed in the same unit. The value of the function is, therefore, simply a *number*, expressed in no units at all. The sides 5, 12, 13 in Fig. 34 could, therefore, just as well be in centimeters, inches, feet, meters, miles, or any unit at all, provided only that the same unit be used for all three sides. Thus, if a is given as 5 inches and b as 1 foot we must first express both in inches or both in feet, but in either unit the value of the function remains the same *for the same angle*.

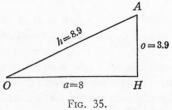

Fig. 35.

Let us find the values of the three chief functions of the angles in Fig. 35, where o, a, h represent the legs *o*pposite and *a*djacent to angle O (this does not mean "zero") and the *h*ypotenuse, and O, A, H the corresponding opposite angles, H being the right angle.

We have

$$\sin O = \frac{o}{h} = \frac{3.9}{8.9} = 0.438,$$

$$\cos O = \frac{a}{h} = \frac{8.0}{8.9} = .899,$$

$$\tan O = \frac{o}{a} = \frac{3.9}{8.0} = .488,$$

and

$$\sin A = \frac{a}{h} = \frac{8.0}{8.9} = .899,$$

$$\cos A = \frac{o}{h} = \frac{3.9}{8.9} = .438,$$

$$\tan A = \frac{a}{o} = \frac{8.0}{3.9} = 2.050.$$

Suppose we have to calculate the functions of the angle A of a triangle ABC when we are given only the legs a, b; how shall we proceed without knowing the hypotenuse c? The answer to this question is given by equation (5a), article 6, which states that

$$c^2 = a^2 + b^2. \tag{5a}$$

Thus, suppose we are given $a = 8$, $b = 15$, to find $\sin A$, $\cos A$ and $\tan A$. Using the above equation we first find c as follows:

$$c^2 = (8)^2 + (15)^2 = 64 + 225 = 289,$$

$$\therefore \quad c = \sqrt{289} = 17.$$

We now have the three sides $a = 8$, $b = 15$, $c = 17$ and the functions are found in the usual manner. We get

$$\sin A = \frac{a}{c} = \frac{8}{17} = .470,$$

$$\cos A = \frac{b}{c} = \frac{15}{17} = .883,$$

$$\tan A = \frac{a}{b} = \frac{8}{15} = .533.$$

Using the same values of a, b, c and the appropriate formulas the functions of B are as easily found. This is left as an exercise for the reader.

If we know the hypotenuse and either leg of a right triangle but do not know the other leg, it may be found by means of equation (5a) by proper transposition.   Thus, since

$$\left. \begin{array}{l} c^2 = a^2 + b^2, \\ a^2 = c^2 - b^2, \\ b^2 = c^2 - a^2. \end{array} \right\} \qquad (5b)$$

then

With the legs known, the first of these formulas will give the hypotenuse.   With the hypotenuse c and the leg b known the second will give the leg a, and with the hypotenuse and leg a known the third will give b.   By means of the formulas (5b), therefore, when any two of the sides of a right triangle are known we can at once find the third, and with all three sides known the functions of either or both acute angles of the right triangle can then be calculated immediately by means of the function formulas.

In the following article are given exercises similar to those worked out in this article.   The reader should work each example by direct calculation from the triangle and check the results by comparing the corresponding functions and co-functions of the acute angles and also by the use of the relation $\tan x = \dfrac{\sin x}{\cos x}$.

10. Exercises.

In each of the following exercises c represents the hypotenuse and the other two letters the legs of a right triangle.   Draw a figure for each and indicate angles opposite the respective sides by the corresponding capital letters.   From the two given sides in each find the third side and then calculate the sine, cosine and tangent of angle A of each triangle.   Carry the results to two decimal places.

1. $c = 10$	3. $a = 15$	5. $a = 7$
$b = 6$	$b = 36$	$c = 25$
$a =$	$c =$	$b =$
2. $c = 30$	4. $a = 16$	6. $c = 41$
$a = 24$	$b = 30$	$b = 40$
$b =$	$c =$	$a =$

Chapter 3

VALUES OF FUNCTIONS
OF ACUTE ANGLES.
TRIGONOMETRIC TABLES

11. Functions of 45°. If, in the square *ACBD* of Fig. 36, the diagonal *AB* be drawn, it will divide the square (which is a parallelogram) into two equal right triangles, and since the legs of these right triangles are the equal sides of the square, and the hypotenuse of each

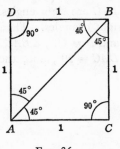

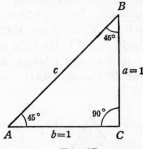

FIG. 36.   FIG. 37.

is the diagonal *AB*, the two acute angles in each triangle will be equal and half of 90°. If, therefore, the sides of the square are taken as equal to 1 in any desired unit of measurement and the right triangle *ABC* is drawn separately, it will be as shown in Fig. 37.

In the right △*ABC* of Fig. 37 we have by equation (5a),

$$c^2 = a^2 + b^2 = 1^2 + 1^2 = 2.$$

$$\therefore \quad c = \sqrt{2} = 1.414\ldots,$$

and the three chief functions of the angle $A = B = 45°$ are,

$$\sin 45° = \frac{1}{1.414} = .7071\ldots,$$

39

$$\cos 45° = \frac{1}{1.414} = .7071\ldots,$$

$$\tan 45° = \frac{1}{1} = 1.0000.$$

Thus, the sine and cosine of 45° are the same and equal $\frac{1}{\sqrt{2}}$ while the tangent of 45° is exactly 1. These results could be seen at once because the legs of the 45° triangle are equal.

The 45° triangle is very important and useful and the functions of 45° should be committed to memory.

12. Functions of 30° and 60°. The equilateral triangle has been seen to be also equiangular and each angle is 60°. (See (J), article 5.) In the equilateral triangle *ABD* of Fig. 38 the altitude *AC* drawn through the vertex *A* is, by definition of the *altitude*, perpendicular to the base *BD* and, hence, the two angles at *C* are right angles. The two triangles *ABC*, *ADC* are, therefore, right triangles. Then, since $\angle B + \angle BAC = 90°$ in the right triangle and $B = 60°$, $\angle BAC = 30°$. Similarly, in the right triangle *ACD*, $\angle DAC = 30°$, and, therefore, the altitude *AC* bisects $\angle BAD$.

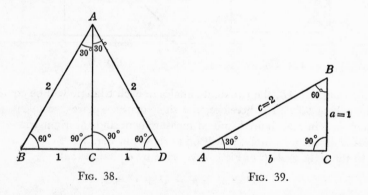

Fig. 38.   Fig. 39.

Since the right triangles *ABC*, *ADC* have equal angles, equal hypotenuses, and one leg *AC* the same, the triangles are congruent, and the corresponding legs *BC* and *DC* are equal. The altitude *AC*, therefore, also bisects the base. If, therefore, the sides of the $\triangle ABD$ be taken equal to 2 units, we have $BC = DC = 1$ and the right triangle *ABC* drawn separately with *AC* as base is as shown in Fig. 39.

In $\triangle ABC$, Fig. 39, we have $a = 1$, $c = 2$, and by equations (5b)

$$b^2 = c^2 - a^2 = 4 - 1 = 3.$$

$$\therefore \quad b = \sqrt{3} = 1.7320 \ldots$$

Therefore, from Fig. 39, the functions of 30° and 60° are

$$\sin 30° = \frac{1}{2} \qquad = .5000,$$

$$\cos 30° = \frac{1.7320}{2} = .8660 \ldots,$$

$$\tan 30° = \frac{1}{1.7320} = .5774 \ldots,$$

and

$$\sin 60° = \cos 30° = .8660 \ldots,$$

$$\cos 60° = \sin 30° = .5000,$$

$$\tan 60° = \frac{1.7320}{1} = 1.7320 \ldots.$$

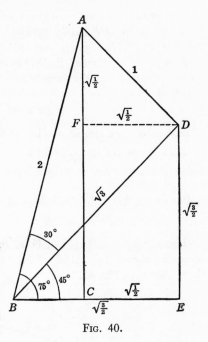

Fig. 40.

The 30°–60° triangle is also of great importance and wide usefulness. The 30–60° and 45° triangles are both cut from transparent sheet material such as celluloid for use by draftsmen and both can easily be laid out by means of the carpenter's square. The 45° triangle is easily remembered and drawn because of its legs being equal, and so is the 30–60° because of the fact that the leg opposite the 30° angle is exactly half the hypotenuse.

13. **Functions of 15° and 75°.**   In Fig. 40, the 30–60° right triangle ABD is drawn with the leg $AD = 1$ and hypotenuse $AB = 2$, and the 45° triangle BDE is drawn with $BD = \sqrt{3}$ as hypotenuse.   Then $\angle EBA = 45° + 30° = 75°$.   If, then, AC is drawn perpendicular to BE the angles at C are right angles and $\triangle ABC$ is the 15–75° right triangle.

Since $AB = 2$ is already known, it is only necessary to find AC and BC in order to calculate the functions of 15° and 75° directly from the triangle ABC.   This we now proceed to do.

In right $\triangle BDE$, $\overline{BE}^2 + \overline{DE}^2 = \overline{BD}^2 = 3$, and, since $DE = BE$, $BE^2 + \overline{DE}^2 = 2\overline{BE}^2$. Hence, $2\overline{BE}^2 = 3$ and $\overline{BE}^2 = \frac{3}{2}$

$$\therefore \quad BE = \sqrt{\tfrac{3}{2}} = DE.$$

These values are shown on the figure (Fig. 40).

Now draw $DF \perp AC$, making $\triangle AFD$ a right triangle with hypotenuse AD. Then, since $\angle BAD = 60°$ and $\angle BAC = 15°$, $\angle DAF = 45°$. Hence, $\triangle AFD$ is the 45° right triangle with hypotenuse $AD = 1$. In the same manner as above for $\triangle BDE$, therefore, we find

$$AF = \sqrt{\tfrac{1}{2}} = FD.$$

These values are also shown in the figure.

Now $AC = AF + FC$ and $FC = DE = \sqrt{\tfrac{3}{2}}$. Therefore,

$$AC = \sqrt{\tfrac{3}{2}} + \sqrt{\tfrac{1}{2}}. \tag{17a}$$

Also, $BC = BE - CE$ and $CE = FD = \sqrt{\tfrac{1}{2}}$. Therefore,

$$BC = \sqrt{\tfrac{3}{2}} - \sqrt{\tfrac{1}{2}}. \tag{17b}$$

Using these results (17a), (17b) for the lengths of AC and BC and drawing the triangle ABC of Fig. 40 separately, the 15–75° triangle is as shown in Fig. 41.

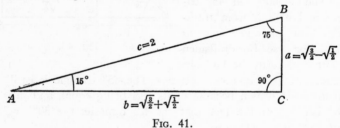

FIG. 41.

The functions of 15° and 75° may now be calculated directly from Fig. 41. Converting the radicals to decimals we have $\sqrt{\tfrac{3}{2}} = 1.2247$ and $\sqrt{\tfrac{1}{2}} = .7071$. We have, therefore, for the functions:

$$\sin 15° = \frac{(\sqrt{\tfrac{3}{2}} - \sqrt{\tfrac{1}{2}})}{2} = \frac{.5176\ldots}{2} = .2588\ldots,$$

$$\cos 15° = \frac{(\sqrt{\tfrac{3}{2}} + \sqrt{\tfrac{1}{2}})}{2} = \frac{1.9318\ldots}{2} = .9659\ldots,$$

$$\tan 15° = \frac{(\sqrt{\tfrac{3}{2}} - \sqrt{\tfrac{1}{2}})}{(\sqrt{\tfrac{3}{2}} + \sqrt{\tfrac{1}{2}})} = \frac{.5176\ldots}{1.9318\ldots} = .2679\ldots,$$

and

$$\sin 75° = \cos 15° \qquad\qquad\qquad = .9659\ldots,$$

$$\cos 75° = \sin 15° \qquad\qquad\qquad = .2588\ldots,$$

$$\tan 75° = \cot 15° \qquad = \frac{1}{.2679\ldots} = 3.7321\ldots.$$

The last three values may be verified by the reader by direct calculation from the triangle.

14. Circular Representation of the Angle Functions.   The angle functions are simple *numbers* without dimensions but they can be represented by the lengths of *lines* drawn to scale by choosing a unit of length and drawing right triangles in a certain manner, and for many purposes this method is useful.   We now proceed to investigate this manner of representing the functions.

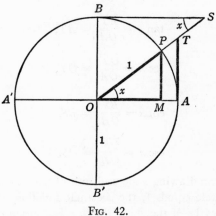

Fig. 42.

Choosing the unit of length, such that in Fig. 42, $OA = 1$, the circle $ABA'B'$ is drawn with center at O and radius OA.   Draw the horizontal diameter AA' and the diameter $BB' \perp AA'$.   In the same manner as in Fig. 8, article 1, let the radius OP, Fig. 42, be a *rotating line* which starts from the *initial position* OA.   At any *terminal position* OP it has then generated the angle $AOP = x$.   As in Fig. 7, the terminal position of the rotating radius may be in either of the four quadrants, so that as the point P moves around the circle in the sense or direction $ABA'B'A$, the rotating radius may generate an angle $AOP = x$ of any magnitude. For the purposes of the present discussion we will let OP lie in the first quadrant so that x is less than or equal to 90°.

Construct right triangles by extending OP beyond the circumference of the circle and drawing $BS \perp OB$ to meet OP at S, and $AT \perp AO$ to meet OS at T, and draw $PM \perp OA$. The triangles OMP, OAT, OBS are then right triangles, and, since $\angle BOS$ is the complement of x and also the complement of $\angle BSO$, then $\angle BSO = x$, as indicated in the figure.

Since $OA = OP = OB = 1$ we have in the right triangles OMP and OAT,

$$\sin x = \frac{\overline{PM}}{\overline{OP}} = PM,$$

$$\cos x = \frac{\overline{OM}}{\overline{OP}} = OM,$$

$$\tan x = \frac{\overline{AT}}{\overline{OA}} = AT,$$

$$\sec x = \frac{\overline{OT}}{\overline{OA}} = OT,$$

and in $\triangle SBO$,

$$\cot x = \frac{\overline{BS}}{\overline{OB}} = BS,$$

$$\csc x = \frac{\overline{OS}}{\overline{OB}} = OS.$$

Thus, when the drawing scale and unit of length are such that the radius of the circle equals 1, the six angle functions are numerically equal to the lengths of the stated lines. The circle of Fig. 42 with radius equal to 1 is called the *unit circle*.

The three chief functions are indicated by the heavy lines:

$$\begin{cases} \sin x = PM, \\ \cos x = OM, \\ \tan x = AT. \end{cases}$$

On account of the relation of the angle functions to the unit circle, they are sometimes called the *circular functions*. Historically, the functions were first studied in connection with the circle rather than as right triangle ratios and were related to an *arc* (portion of a circle) of the circle rather than with an angle at the center of the circle.   It is from these relations that the functions received their names.

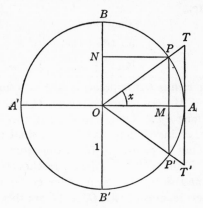

Fig. 43.

Note.   If, in Fig. 42, the line *PM* is extended downward until it meets the circle in a second point *P'* corresponding to *P* and the lines *OP'* and *AT'* are drawn corresponding to *OP* and *OT*, we have Fig. 43.   This figure will show the original method of treating the functions.

In the study of circles in geometry, a line which just touches a circle at one point is called a *tangent* line, from the Latin *tangere*, "to touch."   Therefore, in Fig. 43 the line *TT'* is tangent to the circle at the point *A*.   The curved line *PAP* is the *arc* (arch) corresponding to the angle *POP'* which the arc is said to *subtend* and the line *PMP'* is called a *chord*.   The arc and chord are related as are a bow and its string (cord) and when the string is drawn back against the breast into the position *POP'* to shoot the arrow *OA* the chord or its arc determines the angle *POP'*.

From the facts that *TAT'* is a *tangent* line to the arc at *A* and the Latin word for "breast" (or bosom) is *sinus*, the lines *TT'* and *PP'* were called the *tangent* and the *sinus* of the arc *PAP'* and later of the angle *POP'*.   When the properties of the right triangles *OMP*, *OAT* and their ratios began to be applied, the angle *POA* and the lines *PM* and *TA* instead of ∠*POP'*, *PP'*, *TT'* were found to be more useful.   *TA* and *PM* were then called the tangent and sine of the arc *AP* and of the angle *AOP* = *x*.   If the line *PN* is drawn perpendicular to *OB*, it is the sine of ∠*POB* which is the complement or co-angle of *x* and, therefore, *PN*, or its equal *OM*, is the *co-sine* of *x*.

15. Functions of 0° and 90°.   If the rotating radius *OP* in the unit circle (Fig. 42) is brought down toward the initial position *OA* the angle x decreases until, when the initial position is reached, OP lies on OA and the angle $x = 0$. When this position is reached $\overline{PM} = 0$ and $\overline{AT} = 0$ but M then coincides with A and $\overline{OM} = 1$. The lengths of these lines PM, OM, AT are then the sine, cosine and tangent of $0°$. We have, therefore,

$$\sin 0° = 0,$$

$$\cos 0° = 1,$$

$$\tan 0° = 0.$$

As the rotating radius OP approaches OB as terminal position, P approaches B, and M approaches the center O while T continues to rise indefinitely along AT. Thus, as OP approaches indefinitely near to OB, AT increases indefinitely and without limit and becomes infinitely great. This is expressed by saying that $\overline{AT} = \infty$. The symbol ∞ is read "infinity." As OP finally reaches OB, $\angle AOP = 90°$, $\overline{PM} = OB = 1$, and since M is then at the center O, the length of $\overline{OM}$ is zero. These lengths of PM, OM, AT are then the sine, cosine and tangent of $90°$. We have, therefore,

$$\sin 90° = 1,$$

$$\cos 90° = 0,$$

$$\tan 90° = \infty.$$

The values of the functions of $0°$ and $90°$ found in this article together with those already found in articles 11, 12, 13 will later be found to be very useful and instructive.

16. Functions of Acute Angles. The values of the functions of particular angles found in articles 11, 12, 13, 15 are collected in Table II below. In this table the angles expressed in degrees are

TABLE II

Angle	sin	cos	tan
0°	0	1.0000	0
15	.2588	.9659	.2679
30	.5000	.8660	.5774
45	.7071	.7071	1.0000
60	.8660	.5000	1.7320
75	.9659	.2588	3.7321
90	1.0000	0	∞

given in the column headed "Angle" and the corresponding functions are given on the same line with the angle in the adjacent columns headed "sin," "cos," "tan."

This table shows that the sines of acute angles are less than 1 and in the complete first quadrant both sines and cosines range from zero to 1. The *sine increases* as the angle increases but the *cosine decreases* as the angle increases. The tangent, like the sine, increases with the angle, but instead of varying from zero to 1, it varies from zero to infinity. This variation is made visible and easily studied in the *unit circle* (Fig. 42) by allowing the generating line OP to rotate from the initial position OA to OB. The angle x is thus made to vary from zero to 90° and the changes in the functions sine, cosine, tangent are represented by the changes in the lengths of the lines PM, OM, AT.

By drawing the unit circle to a convenient scale and setting the line OP at values of x in degrees, by means of a protractor, the values of the functions may be read approximately (depending on the size of the diagram) on a ruler or scale as the corresponding lengths of the lines PM, OM, AT. The values may also be found, approximately, by drawing right triangles of any convenient size with the angles laid off by means of the protractor, and calculating the ratios of the measured sides by means of the fundamental formulas of Table I as in articles 11, 12, 13.

Both of these methods illustrate vividly the meaning and relations of the functions, but they are too slow and inaccurate for finding the values of functions of all angles. For calculating the functions of all angles by minutes and seconds, and to as many decimal places as desired, special equations and formulas are derived in higher mathematics.*

17. Trigonometric Tables. Table II forms a partially complete table of the angle or trigonometric functions. Such tables are called *trigonometric tables*. Table II gives the values of the three functions to four decimal places for every fifteen degrees from zero to 90°. Trigonometric tables suited to different purposes have been constructed which give the values of the functions to many more decimal places and for every degree and minute or even every second of angle. Tables of eight and ten decimal places for every second are needed in astronomy. Six-place or seven-place tables for every ten seconds are

---

* See the author's "Calculus for the Practical Man," Chapter XIX (D. Van Nostrand Co. Inc.).

used in surveying. For some branches of science and engineering, and for ordinary calculations, four-place and five-place tables for each minute of angle are satisfactory. Such tables are printed in a variety of forms, some showing in adjacent columns all the functions of the same angle, like Table II, and others showing the different functions in separate parts of the table printed on different pages.

Since the trigonometric functions are ordinary numbers and may be used in the same manner as other numbers, after they are known, we may also use their logarithms. Thus, the logarithm of the sine of 45° is log .7071 = 9.8495 − 10 = $\bar{1}$.8495, the minus sign over the 1 indicating that it applies only to 1, the mantissa .8495 being positive. (This notation for logarithms is less commonly used today than the form 9.8495 − 10, which is more consistent with standard mathematical usage.) This is usually written log sin 45° = 9.8495, the −10 being understood to follow, as all except log sin 90° have negative characteristics. In order to avoid the necessity of looking into the trigonometric tables for the function (number) and then looking in the logarithm table for its logarithm, tables of logarithms of the functions have been prepared. These are arranged and printed like the tables of the functions and the columns headed the same way, but instead of the figures in the columns being the functions themselves, they are the logarithms of the functions. The logarithms of sines, cosines, etc., are called *logarithmic sines*, *logarithmic cosines*, etc., and in order to distinguish the logarithmic functions from the actual values of the functions themselves, the functions are called the *natural functions*. We thus have the *natural sines*, *natural cosines*, etc.

A four-place table of natural sines, cosines and tangents and a similar four-place table of the logarithmic functions of every minute of angle from zero to 90° are given at the end of this book. In each table the sines, cosines and tangents are printed separately and each part fills two pages which face one another, angles up to 45° being given on the first page and angles above 45° on the second page. These tables are to be used in the next chapter and the method of their use is described below.

18. How to Use the Trigonometric Tables. Since the printing and general method of use of the trigonometric tables in this book are the same for all, only the tables of natural sines will be described. Remarks concerning certain small differences in detail will be given after this description.

The degrees of angle are in the first column at the left of the page, 0–44° on the first page and 45–90° on the second. Immediately at the right of the number giving the number of degrees is the function; thus, in the sine table beside 12° is found 2079. No decimal point is printed but a decimal point is to be placed before each sine; thus, sin 12° = .2079. Similarly, sin 1° = .0175, sin 78° = .9781. On the same line with each number of degrees, reaching across the page, are the sines of that number of degrees plus different numbers of minutes, the number of minutes being given at the top of each column. Thus, the sine of the angle $12\frac{1}{2}$° or 12° 30′ is on the line with 12° and in the column headed 30′, and the figures are 2164; sin 12° 30′ = .2164. Similarly, the sine of 48′ or sin 0° 48′ = .0140, and sin 78° 6′ = .9785.

Columns are given for each six minutes, 0′, 6′, 12′, 18′, 24′, etc. In order to find the sines for numbers of minutes not given in these columns, separate columns are given at the right of the page which contain the numbers to be added to those given in the main columns for each 1, 2, 3, 4 or 5 additional minutes. Thus, in order to find sin 78° 9′ we must find what is to be added to the number which is sin 78° 6′. 78° 9′ is 3′ more than 78° 6′ and on the line with 78° in the column at the right of the page headed 3 we find 2. This 2 is to be added to the last figures of the sine of 78° 6′ which is .9785, giving .9787; thus, sin 78° 9′ = .9787. Similarly, sin 78° 3′ = (sin 78° 0′) + (difference for 3′) = .9781 + 2 = .9783; sin 59′ = sin 0° 59′ = (sin 0° 54′) + (dif. for 5′) = .0157 + 15 = .0172; sin 45° 43′ = .7157 + 2 = .7159; sin 12° 35′ = .2178.

Natural cosines are found in the manner described for sines except that the differences in the columns at the right of the page are to be *subtracted* instead of added. This is due to the fact that the cosine decreases as the angle increases, as appears in the table and as was first noted in Table II, article 16.

Natural tangents are also found in the manner described for sines when the angle is less than 45°. For 45–90°, however, the decimals in all columns after the first are to have inserted before the decimal point, the number appearing before the decimal point in the first column on the same line. Thus, tan 53° 36′ = 1.3564. Similarly, tan 73° 52′ = 3.4564, the 4564 being found in the usual manner.

If the decimal part of a tangent has a dash over the first figure the number appearing before the decimal point in the first column of the *next* line is to be used. Thus, for tan 71° 48′ we find on the 71° line and in the 48′ column 0̄415. Before this we are to write 3 instead of the 2 which appears beside the 71°; this gives tan 71° 48′ = 3.0415. Similarly, tan 63° 32′ = 2.0086, the 0086 being found in the usual manner.

If we are told or find from calculation that the sine of a certain angle is .2588, we find from Table II, article 16, that the angle which has this sine is 15°. Similarly, the angle whose tangent is 3.7321 is 75°, as seen from the same table. This is found by locating the given sine or tangent in the body of the table and looking for the number of degrees on the same line in the column at the left of the table. In the same way we find, from the tables at the end of the book, the angle in degrees corresponding to any sine, cosine or tangent. In addition, we find the minutes, if any, by looking at the top of the column in which the given function is located. Thus, the angle whose sine is .5878 is 36°; the angle which has the cosine .3811 is 67° 36′; and the angle whose tangent is 1.1792 is 49° 42′, the 1. being found in the first column on the 49° line and the 1792 in the 42′ column on the same line.

If the exact function is not found in the table, the next smaller number is located and the corresponding angle read. To this angle is then added (for sines or tangents, subtracted for cosines) the number of minutes at the head of the difference column on the right which contains on the same line the difference between the given value and the smaller value located in the table. Thus, if the sine of a certain angle is .3657 we cannot locate this number in the table directly. The next smaller number which we can find is .3649 which corresponds to 21° 24′, and the difference is 3657 − 3649 = 8, which on the same line in the difference column corresponds to 3 minutes. The angle sought is, therefore, 21° 24′ + 3′ = 21° 27′.

The tables of *logarithmic functions* are used in the same manner as are those of the natural functions, the characteristics (figure before the decimal point) being found as in the table of natural tangents. After each function as taken from the table is to be written −10, as indicated in the note at the bottom of each page of the logarithmic tables. Thus, the logarithmic sine of 41° 12′ as read in the table is 9.8187 and with the −10 appended this is written: log sin 41° 12′ = 9.8187 − 10.

19. Exercises.

Find, from the tables, the natural sine, cosine and tangent of each of the angles in the following chart and write it in the space indicated or on a separate sheet ruled in the same way:

gle.......	17° 18′	53° 54′	48′	30°	17° 20′	53° 59′	89° 59′
e.........							
ine.......							
gent......							

nd, from the tables, the angles corresponding to the sines, cosines and ents given in the following chart, and write them in the spaces indicated e *angle* on the chart or on a separate sheet.

e..........	.4099	.....	.....	.8851	.....	....	.0143	.....	......
ine........	.....	.9239	.....	.....	.5110	......	....	.0203	......
gent......	.....	.....	.4559	.....	.....	9.0579	.....	.....	2.4182
gle.......									

nd, from the tables, the logarithmic sine, cosine and tangent of each of angles in the following chart and write it in the space indicated or on a rate sheet:

gle........	12° 12′	44° 59′	73° 1′	0° 50′	45°	89° 59′
sin........						
cos........						
tan........						

ind, from the tables, the angles corresponding to the logarithmic sines, nes and tangents given in the following chart, and write them in the spaces cated for the *angle* on the chart or on a separate sheet.

sin........	9.9614	......	......	9.5071	......	......
cos........	......	9.6356	......	......	9.8748	......
tan........	......	,......	9.6746	......	......	10.5527
gle........						

Chapter 4

RIGHT TRIANGLE CALCULATIONS

20. Introduction. In problems which involve straight lines, angles and circles it is frequently necessary to find one or more lengths, distances or angles when certain lengths, distances or angles are known. If an algebraic equation or a formula containing the desired quantity can be found, the solution of the problem is then simple, requiring only computation. This is usually performed very readily either mentally, manually by ordinary arithmetic, with the slide rule, or by means of logarithms.

Problems involving lines, distances and angles can generally be represented by a sketch and such a figure can also frequently be laid out in or divided into right triangles by drawing certain additional lines. The solution of the problem is thus reduced to a right triangle calculation involving sides and angles and we have a number of formulas which contain these parts of triangles. These are the fundamental trigonometric function formulas.

As an example, suppose it is desired to support a post or pole of a certain known height by means of a tight guy wire fastened at the top of the pole and also to a stake at a certain known distance from the foot of the pole on level ground. How long a wire is required, and how will it be inclined to the ground and to the pole? This problem is easily solved by means of the trigonometric function formulas.

In Fig. 44, let DL represent the pole and h its known height. Let DH represent the wire which is fastened to the stake at H, and let l represent its length. Let d represent the distance LH of the stake from the foot L of the pole. Then, DLH is a right triangle and we know that $l^2 = d^2 + h^2$ and, hence, $l = \sqrt{d^2 + h^2}$. As both d and h are known, l can be calculated from this formula at once. The inclination of the wire to the ground is the $\angle DHL$, or simply $\angle H$, and from the fundamental formula $\tan = (\text{opp}) \div (\text{adj})$ we have $\tan H = h/d$. Since both h and d are known, the tangent of $\angle H$ is found at once from this formula, and with the tangent thus known, the angle of inclination H is read from the table. With H known the angle $D = 90° - H$.

52

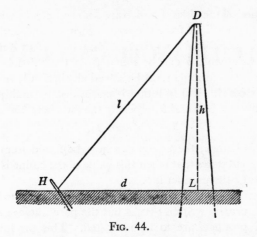

FIG. 44.

The length l of the wire can also be found without using the tedious square root formula. For, with the $\angle H$ known from the formula $\tan H = h/d$ as just described, we can use the formula $\sin H = h/l$. From this, by algebraic transformation, l is given by $l = h \div (\sin H)$ and $\sin H$ is found at once from the table for use in this formula. After finding H, the $\angle D$ is found as stated above.

Thus, by selecting the appropriate one of the fundamental right triangle formulas and properly transforming it according to the methods of algebra, we have at our command equations and formulas for calculating any side or angle of a right triangle when sufficient original information or *data* are given.

21. Transformation of the Right Triangle Formulas. When the sides and angles of any right triangle are indicated in the usual manner by a, b, c and A, B, C, respectively, C being the right angle and c the hypotenuse, the fundamental formulas of the right triangle are,

$$\left. \begin{array}{l} A + B = 90°, \\[2mm] \sin A = \dfrac{a}{c}, \\[2mm] \cos A = \dfrac{b}{c}, \\[2mm] \tan A = \dfrac{a}{b}, \end{array} \right\} \qquad (18)$$

with corresponding function formulas for the angle B.

If the values of the sides a and c are known, $\angle A$ can be found at once by calculating $\sin A$ from the second formula and finding A from the table; B is then found from the first formula. With A now known, and c given originally, b can be found from the third formula. In order to find b, this formula must be solved algebraically for b in terms of c and A or $\cos A$. This solution is performed by multiplying both sides of the formula by c and transposing the members, the result being

$$b = c \times (\cos A),$$

and since A is known, the cosine can now be found from the table. The formula then states that when this value of the cosine is multiplied by the value of c the product is b.

The product of c and the cosine of A which is indicated above by $c \times (\cos A)$ is usually written $c \cos A$ but the parentheses may be used when special products are to be indicated. This product is never written $\cos Ac$, as this would mean the cosine of $(A \cdot c)$. The same method is used in writing products of any of the functions by the sides or other algebraic symbols.

Thus, the solution of the third of formulas (18) for b gives $b = c \cos A$. Similarly, it may be transformed to give $c = \dfrac{b}{\cos A}$, which means that c is equal to the quotient of b by the cosine of A.

By similar algebraic operations, each of the formulas (18) may be transformed so as to express each of the quantities it contains (side or angle, or angle function) in terms of the other one or two quantities in it. Thus, from the first formula we have,

$$A = 90° - B, \quad B = 90° - A, \tag{19}$$

and from the second,

$$a = c \sin A, \qquad c = \frac{a}{\sin A}.$$

Similarly

$$b = c \cos A, \qquad c = \frac{b}{\cos A},$$

$$a = b \tan A, \qquad b = \frac{a}{\tan A}. \tag{20}$$

Formulas (20), (19) and the last three of (18) enable us to find any one of the sides or angles on the left side of each when those on the right side of the formula are known.

The reader should verify the formulas (20) by carrying out step by step the indicated algebraic transformations of (18).

22. Solution of Right Triangles.   In the example given in article 20, it was seen that with the legs of the triangle known, the hypotenuse and both acute angles could be found.   Similarly, in formulas (18), (19), and (20), if the values of any side and angle, or any two sides are known, the remaining sides and angle or side and angles can be found.   The sides and angles of a triangle are called its *parts*, and, when some of the parts of a triangle are found by calculation from known parts, the triangle is said to be *solved*, by analogy with the solving of equations for unknown quantities in terms of known quantities.   Thus, the above results are expressed by saying that when two parts of a right triangle are given, of which at least one must be a side, the triangle can be completely solved.   One of the given parts must be a side because two angles alone do not completely determine a triangle.   Two angles merely determine the shape and not the dimensions.

In order to solve a right triangle, the values of the known parts are first noted and either tabulated as data or indicated on a figure, and the unknown parts are listed or also indicated on the same figure. The formulas which contain the known quantities, together with only one unknown quantity in each, are selected and written down in the proper form.   The unknown parts are then calculated by substituting in these formulas the values of the known parts and carrying out the computations as indicated.   The computations are to be performed by ordinary arithmetic, the slide rule, or logarithms, as determined by the requirements of the problem and the time available, or by choice or instructions.

There are five combinations of two sides, or an angle and a side, which may occur (one angle being always a right angle).   These are

> I. Two legs.
> II. One leg and hypotenuse.
> III. One angle and opposite leg.
> IV. One angle and adjacent leg.
> V. One angle and hypotenuse.

Where "one leg" or "one angle" is cited this may be either leg or either acute angle.

These five cases will be taken up in turn and their solutions explained in detail in the next article, an illustrative solution being worked out in full for each. In these examples, the standard notation a, b, c and A, B, C will be used, C, c being the right angle and hypotenuse. In actual problems the sides and angles may be denoted by any symbols whatever. The lengths of the sides may be expressed in any unit whatever, provided the same unit is used for all three. In the following solutions, no unit will be given but the same unit is understood for all three sides in each.

23. Illustrative Examples.

Case I. Given the two legs: a, b (Fig. 45).

     Given: $a = 44.6$ *To find:* $A = 52° 36'$

            $b = 34.1$ $B = 37° 24'$

                                          $c = 56.1$

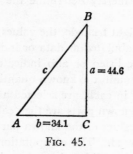

FIG. 45.

Formulas: $\tan A = \dfrac{a}{b}$, $B = 90° - A$, $c = \dfrac{a}{\sin A}$.

CALCULATION

$$\tan A = \frac{44.6}{34.1} = 1.308; \text{ from table } A = 52° 36'.$$

$$B = 90° - 52° 36' = 37° 24'.$$

$$c = \frac{44.6}{\sin 52° 36'} = \frac{44.6}{.7944} = 56.1.$$

The side c may also be found from the formula $c = b/\sin B$.

Case II.   Given, one leg and hypotenuse: *a, c* (Fig. 46).

Given: $a = 11.5$ *To find:* $A = 34°\ 18'$

  $c = 20.4$ $B = 55°\ 42'$

                                  $b = 16.9$

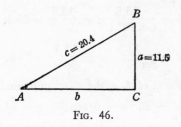

Fig. 46.

Formulas: $\sin A = \dfrac{a}{c}$, $B = 90° - A$, $b = c \cos A$.

CALCULATION

$\sin A = \dfrac{11.5}{20.4} = .564$; from table $A = 34°\ 18'$.

$B = 90° - 34°\ 18' = 55°\ 42'$.

$b = 20.4 \cos 34°\ 18' = 20.4 \times .8261 = 16.9$.

If the leg *b* instead of *a* is given, the solution formulas are,

$\cos A = b/c$, $B = 90° - A$, $a = c \sin A$.

Case III.   Given, one angle and opposite leg: *A, a* (Fig. 47).

Given: $A = 30°\ 19'$ *To find:* $B = 59°\ 41'$

  $a = 13.5$ $b = 23.1$

                                  $c = 26.8$

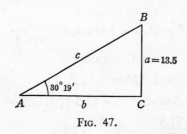

Fig. 47.

Formulas: $B = 90° - A, \; b = \dfrac{a}{\tan A}, \; c = \dfrac{a}{\sin A}.$

CALCULATION

$$B = 90° - 30° \; 19' = 59° \; 41'.$$

$$b = \frac{13.5}{\tan 30° \; 19'} = \frac{13.5}{.5847} = 23.1.$$

$$c = \frac{13.5}{\sin 30° \; 19'} = \frac{13.5}{.5048} = 26.8.$$

If B, b are given instead of A, a, the solution formulas are:

$$A = 90° - B, \quad a = b/\tan B, \quad c = b/\sin B.$$

Case IV. Given, one angle and adjacent leg: A, b (Fig. 48).

<table>
<tr><td>Given: $A = 53° \; 8'$</td><td>To find: $B = 36° \; 52'$</td></tr>
<tr><td>$b = 51.5$</td><td>$a = 68.6$</td></tr>
<tr><td></td><td>$c = 85.8$</td></tr>
</table>

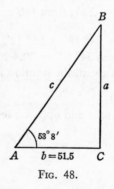

FIG. 48.

Formulas: $B = 90° - A, \; a = b \tan A, \; c = \dfrac{b}{\cos A}.$

CALCULATION

$$B = 90° - 53° \; 8' = 36° \; 52'.$$

$$a = 51.5 \tan 53° \; 8' = 51.5 \times 1.3335 = 68.6$$

$$c = \frac{51.5}{\cos 53° \; 8'} = \frac{51.5}{.6000} = 85.8.$$

f B, a are given instead of A, b, the solution formulas are:

$$A = 90° - B, \quad b = a \tan B, \quad c = a/\cos B.$$

Case V. Given, one angle and hypotenuse: A, c (Fig. 49).

Given: $A = 26° 16'$	*To find:* $B = 63° 44'$
$c = 25.4$	$a = 11.2$
	$b = 22.8$

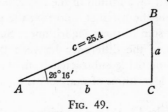

FIG. 49.

Formulas: $B = 90° - A$, $a = c \sin A$, $b = c \cos A$.

CALCULATION

$B = 90° - 26° 16' = 63° 44'$.

$a = 25.4 \sin 26° 16' = 25.4 \times .4425 = 11.23$.

$b = 25.4 \cos 26° 16' = 25.4 \times .8967 = 22.8$.

f B, c instead of A, c are given, the solution formulas are:

$$A = 90° - B, \quad a = c \cos B, \quad b = c \sin B.$$

This completes the solution of all the cases of right triangles.

In this article the computations have been performed with the slide ule, the functions and angles being read from the tables in this book. After the values of the functions are known, the multiplications and ivisions may, of course, be carried out by ordinary arithmetic but hen the data are given to only three figures, or to the nearest minute, he slide rule gives sufficient precision. If the reader desires to use the lide rule, full descriptions and explanations of the methods of its use ill be found in books on the slide rule.* In such books will be ound not only descriptions of the simple methods of multiplication nd division as used in the above solutions, but also methods of obtain- ig the angles and functions directly from the slide rule without the se of the tables.

* See the author's "A Manual of the Slide Rule" (D. Van Nostrand Co. Inc.).

If the data are given to four or more figures, greater precision is obtained by the use of logarithms in the computations. Logarithmic solutions are described and illustrated in the following articles.

24. Logarithmic Solutions. As the reader will require some knowledge of algebra in the study of trigonometry, it is assumed that he has sufficient knowledge of the use of logarithms to perform multiplication and division with them. It is sufficient to recall that logarithmic multiplication is performed by addition of the logarithms of the factors to obtain the logarithm of the product, and that the product is then the anti-logarithm of the sum of these logarithms. Similarly, a quotient is the anti-logarithm of the difference between the logarithms, the logarithm of the divisor being subtracted from that of the dividend. A four-place table of logarithms of numbers is included at the end of this book.

As described in articles 17, 18, the logarithms of the natural trigonometric functions are obtained directly from the tables of the *logarithmic functions*, so that when a number representing the length of a side is to be multiplied or divided by one of the functions, the logarithm of the function may in the usual manner be added to or subtracted from that of the number. If the logarithm of a function is found as the difference between two other logarithms as, for example, when $\sin A = a/c$, $\log \sin A = \log a - \log c$, the *log sin* is located in the table of logarithmic sines and the corresponding angle A read directly in the manner described in article 18.

The logarithmic solution of each of the cases solved by direct computation in article 23 is given in full in the next article.

25. Illustrative Examples: Logarithmic Solution.

Case I. Given, the two legs: a, b.

Given: $a = 78.24$ *To find:* $A = 20° 12'$ *Formulas:* $\tan A = a/b$

$\quad\quad\quad b = 212.6$ $\quad\quad\quad B = 69° 48'$ $\quad\quad\quad\quad\quad B = 90° - A$

$\quad\quad\quad\quad\quad\quad\quad\quad\quad c = 226.5$ $\quad\quad\quad\quad\quad\quad\quad c = a/\sin A$

COMPUTATION

$\log 78.24 = 11.8934 - 10$	$\log 78.24 = 11.8934 - 10$
$-\log 212.6 = 2.3276$	$-\log \sin 20° 12' = 9.5382 - 10$
$\log \tan A = 9.5658 - 10$	$\log c = 2.3552$
$A = 20° 12'$	$c = 226.5$

$$B = 90° - 20° 12' = 69° 48'$$

Case II.   Given, one leg and hypotenuse: b, c.

Given: $b = 31.17$ *To find:* $A = 58° 9'$ *Formulas:* $\cos A = b/c$

$\quad\quad c = 59.08$ $\quad\quad B = 31° 51'$ $\quad\quad\quad B = 90° - A$

$\quad\quad\quad\quad\quad\quad\quad\quad a = 50.18$ $\quad\quad\quad\quad a = c \sin A$

COMPUTATION

$$\begin{array}{ll}
\log 31.17 = 11.4937 - 10 & \log 59.08 = 1.7714 \\
-\log 59.08 = 1.7714 & +\log \sin 58° 9' = 9.9291 - 10 \\
\hline
\log \cos A = 9.7223 - 10 & \log a = 1.7005 \\
\quad\quad A = 58° 9' & \quad\quad a = 50.18
\end{array}$$

$$B = 90° - 58° 9' = 31° 51'$$

Case III.   Given, one angle and opposite leg: B, b.

Given: $B = 62° 20'$ *To find:* $A = 27° 40'$ *Formulas:* $A = 90° - B$

$\quad\quad b = 897.6$ $\quad\quad\quad a = 470.7$ $\quad\quad\quad\quad a = b/\tan B$

$\quad\quad\quad\quad\quad\quad\quad\quad c = 1013$ $\quad\quad\quad\quad\quad c = b/\sin B$

COMPUTATION

$$\begin{array}{ll}
\log 897.6 = 12.9531 - 10 & \log 897.6 = 12.9531 - 10 \\
-\log \tan 62° 20' = 10.2804 - 10 & -\log \sin 62° 20' = 9.9473 - 10 \\
\hline
\log a = 2.6727 & \log c = 3.0058 \\
\quad a = 470.7 & \quad c = 1013
\end{array}$$

$$A = 90° - 62° 20' = 27° 40'$$

Case IV.   Given, one angle and adjacent leg: B, a.

Given: $B = 47° 32'$ *To find:* $A = 42° 28'$ *Formulas:* $A = 90° - B$

$\quad\quad a = 4126$ $\quad\quad\quad\quad b = 4508$ $\quad\quad\quad\quad b = a \tan B$

$\quad\quad\quad\quad\quad\quad\quad\quad c = 6111$ $\quad\quad\quad\quad\quad c = a/\cos B$

COMPUTATION

$$\begin{array}{ll}
\log 4126 = 3.6155 & \log 4126 = 13.6155 - 10 \\
+\log \tan 47° 32' = 10.0385 - 10 & -\log \cos 47° 32' = 9.8294 - 10 \\
\hline
\log b = 3.6540 & \log c = 3.7861 \\
\quad b = 4508. & \quad c = 6111.
\end{array}$$

$$A = 90° - 47° 32' = 42° 28'$$

Case V. Given, one angle and hypotenuse: B, c.

Given: $B = 79° 3'$ *To find:* $A = 10° 57'$ *Formulas:* $A = 90° - B$

$\qquad c = 48.35$ $\qquad\qquad\qquad a = 9.183$ $\qquad\qquad\qquad a = c \cos B$

$\qquad\qquad\qquad\qquad\qquad\quad b = 47.47$ $\qquad\qquad\qquad\quad b = c \sin B$

COMPUTATION

$\log 48.35 = 1.6844$ $\qquad\qquad\qquad \log 48.35 = 1.6844$

$+\log \cos 79° 3' = 9.2786 - 10$ $\qquad +\log \sin 79° 3' = 9.9920 - 10$

$\qquad\quad \log a = \ .9630$ $\qquad\qquad\qquad\quad \log b = 1.6764$

$\qquad\qquad\quad a = 9.183$ $\qquad\qquad\qquad\qquad\quad b = 47.47$

$$A = 90° - 79° 3' = 10° 57'$$

This completes the logarithmic solution of all cases of right triangles.

26. Exercises.

The first ten of the following exercises are to be solved directly by the use of the natural functions. A figure should be drawn for each and the computations may be performed either by arithmetic or with the slide rule. The last eleven are to be solved by the use of logarithms.

In each exercise the standard notation is used and the three parts not named (exclusive of C) are to be found.

1. $B = 49° 8'$ $\quad c = 34.7$	8. $A = 60° 56'$ $\quad a = 34$	15. $a = 998$ $\quad b = 1292$
2. $a = 160$ $\quad c = 281$	9. $b = 613$ $\quad A = 40° 13'$	16. $A = 39° 34'$ $\quad c = 72.15$
3. $a = 4.82$ $\quad b = 2.65$	10. $B = 55° 17'$ $\quad b = 160$	17. $B = 43° 48'$ $\quad b = 50.94$
4. $c = 305$ $\quad A = 63° 31'$	11. $a = 4.799$ $\quad b = 3.845$	18. $B = 45° 25'$ $\quad a = 2.189$
5. $c = 369$ $\quad b = 235$	12. $B = 45° 45'$ $\quad c = .008154$	19. $a = 71.78$ $\quad c = 86.53$
6. $b = 72$ $\quad a = 65$	13. $a = 281$ $\quad B = 35° 18'$	20. $b = 18.26$ $\quad c = 30.69$
7. $a = 3.64$ $\quad B = 69° 24'$	14. $A = 51° 4'$ $\quad a = 4.397$	21. $a = 2.19$ $\quad c = 91.92$

27. Area of a Right Triangle.

It was seen in article 5 that the area of a right triangle is one half the product of the legs. If we use the standard notation and let K represent the area we have, therefore,

$$K = \tfrac{1}{2}ab. \tag{21}$$

If both a and b are known, the area can be found at once from this formula.

If, however, only one leg and the hypotenuse or one leg and an angle are known, the other leg must be found before formula (21) can be used, or, if the hypotenuse and an angle are known, both legs must be found before (21) can be used. From the solution of triangles, however, we know that with any two sides or with an acute angle and a side known, all the remaining parts can be found.

In order to use (21), therefore, it is only necessary to express a and b in terms of the given parts and substitute the results in the formula. The computation then gives the area K.

Suppose A and a are known. From the function formulas we know that $b = a/\tan A$. Therefore, the area is $K = \tfrac{1}{2}a(a/\tan A)$, or

$$K = \frac{1}{2}\frac{a^2}{\tan A}. \tag{22}$$

Similarly, if A and b are given, $a = b \tan A$ and

$$K = \tfrac{1}{2}b^2 \tan A \tag{22a}$$

In the same way, if B and b or B and a are known, we find (as the reader can easily prove),

$$K = \frac{1}{2}\frac{b^2}{\tan B}, \quad \text{or} \quad K = \tfrac{1}{2}a^2 \tan B, \tag{23}$$

respectively.

If the hypotenuse and one angle are given, say c and A, then $a = c \sin A$ and $B = c \cos A$. These values in (21) give

$$K = \tfrac{1}{2}c^2 \sin A \cdot \cos A, \tag{24}$$

which means, $\tfrac{1}{2}c^2 (\sin A)(\cos A)$. If, instead of c and A, we have given c and B, then (24) becomes in the same way,

$$K = \tfrac{1}{2}c^2 \sin B \cdot \cos B. \tag{24a}$$

If one leg and the hypotenuse, say a and c, are known, then by the hypotenuse square formula $b = \sqrt{c^2 - a^2}$ and this value of b in (21) gives $K = \tfrac{1}{2}a\sqrt{c^2 - a^2}$. If the leg b instead of a is known, then b simply replaces a in this formula. Therefore,

$$K = \tfrac{1}{2}a\sqrt{c^2 - a^2} = \tfrac{1}{2}b\sqrt{c^2 - b^2}. \tag{25}$$

With any two sides or any side and angle (except C) given, therefore, the area of any right triangle can be found by using the corresponding one of formulas (21)–(25).

In calculating the area of a triangle, as in solving triangles, the sides must all be expressed in the same unit.   The area is then found in the corresponding unit of square measure.

Calculate the area of the following right triangles, of which the given parts are known:

1. $a = 125$ 4. $A = 29° 8'$ 7. $B = 48° 49'$
   $b = 44$ $b = 12$ $a = 47$

2. $a = 47.55$ 5. $A = 18° 14'$ 8. $A = 34° 28'$
   $c = 58.4$ $a = 7$ $c = 18.75$

3. $b = 21$ 6. $B = 54° 20'$ 9. $B = 44° 4'$
   $c = 35$ $b = 14.4$ $c = 27$

Chapter 5

SOLUTION OF PROBLEMS
BY MEANS OF RIGHT TRIANGLES

28. Measurement of Angles. If any two sides of a right triangle are known, the third side can be found by the hypotenuse-square formula. In many cases in actual measurement, however, only one side of a triangle is accessible. In such cases, an angle may be measured. With a side and an angle thus known, any of the remaining parts can be found by the trigonometric methods of the preceding chapter.

For the measurement of angles, three instruments are in common use, each suitable for a different class of measurements. These are the astronomer's transit telescope, the surveyor's transit and the (navigator's) sextant.

The *astronomer's transit* telescope is mounted on a shaft or axle which is perpendicular to the length of the telescope tube. The shaft is mounted in bearings at its ends and the telescope may be turned about the shaft as axis so as to point upward, downward, horizontally, or in any other direction in a vertical plane. A vertical circle marked in degrees and with the shaft passing through its center turns with the telescope and in any position of the telescope a stationary pointer attached to the frame or mounting indicates on the circle the angle through which the telescope is turned. Thus, if the telescope is sighted on a heavenly body and the angle is read on the circle, and the telescope is then turned and sighted on another heavenly body and the angle read again, the difference between the two readings is the angle between the two lines of sight to the heavenly bodies. The vertex of this angle is the center of the rotating circle which is called the *meridian circle*. The entire arrangement is rigidly and permanently mounted and can be turned horizontally only by turning the entire mounting.

The *surveyor's transit* is a small telescope mounted with a graduated circle on a portable tripod in the same manner as the astronomer's transit telescope, and vertical angles are read with it in a similar manner. In addition, the instrument is provided with a horizontal circle and the telescope can be turned about a vertical axis passing through the center of this circle. By means of this arrangement, horizontal angles can also be read. The instrument is provided with levels so that the two circles may be adjusted to be exactly vertical and horizontal, and the telescope itself can also be leveled so that the line of sight through it is horizontal.

The *sextant* is used on shipboard where the motion of the ship would cause a change of position of the telescope between two successive readings. The angle between the lines of sight to two distant objects is, therefore, found by sighting on both at once. This is done by using two telescopes, both of which cast their images of the distant objects on a single mirror at the same time. When the telescopes are so adjusted that the two images are seen together they are properly sighted and the angle between the two lines of sight is read on the graduated circle (or *sixth* of a circle, whence the name *sextant*). Since the sextant is simply held in the hands while taking a reading and is not mounted, it may be turned so as to read horizontal or vertical angles.

If the line of sight to an object is above the horizontal line which passes through the eye of the observer, the angle between the horizontal and the line of sight is called the *angle of elevation* of the object. If the line of sight is below the horizontal, the corresponding angle is called the *angle of depression* of the object.

When the angle between the lines of sight to two objects is in a horizontal plane the angle is called the *bearing* of one of the objects *from the other*. If one of the lines of sight points due north, the angle made with it by the other line of sight is called simply *the bearing* of the second line. It is given by stating the number of degrees east or west from the north and south line.

In this chapter frequent reference will be made to angles measured as outlined above.

29. Method of Solving Problems. The information or measurements which are taken as basis for the calculation of unknown quantities are called the *data* (singular, *datum*) of the problem and must be fully stated and sufficient to enable the desired calculations to be carried out. The formulas or equations used to calculate the unknown quantities are called *solution formulas*. Frequently the solution formulas for problems which involve right triangles are simply the fundamental function formulas of the right triangle. In other cases he problem may involve more than one right triangle with certain ingles or sides common to all.   In such cases, the simple fundamental ormulas may be used singly and the calculations carried out one by ine, so that the result of one part of the solution is used in the calculaion of another part, and so on, until all the unknown parts are found. f, however, only one part is to be calculated and several steps are equired, repetition may often be avoided and simplification obtained by combining and transforming some of the fundamental formulas lgebraically with other relations among the known parts, so as to obtain *one* formula which gives the desired unknown directly.   If this implification is possible, it should be carried out before the numerical computation is begun.   Such a formula is called the solution formula of the problem.

Before beginning the solution of a problem, a figure should be lrawn which represents both the data and the quantities to be found ind all important parts should be marked and lettered.   The data hould be shown on the figure or separately tabulated, using the ymbols given on the figure.   All formulas and transformations should hen be written out in terms of these symbols and the solution formula or formulas obtained in their final form before actual computation is begun.   The data are then to be substituted in the formulas and the computations carried out by ordinary arithmetic, with the slide rule, or by means of logarithms, as the requirements of the problem may lictate.   Examples of all phases of this procedure will be given in the llustrative problem solutions below.

In studying the fundamental function formulas and the right triangle calculations, we have used the a, b, c, A, B, C notation for sides and ingles and it was sufficient to use the vertex letter of an angle as the lgebraic symbol for the value of the angle itself.   In practical problems, however, it is more convenient to use initial letters or other etters to represent the lengths of lines, and to mark angles as in Fig. 3 or Fig. 7, article 1.   As the letters A, B, C are frequently used to ndicate points or objects on the figure, letters of the Greek alphabet ire often used to denote angles.   Thus we refer to the angle α, β, δ, θ, ϕ, etc. (pronounced *alpha*, *beta*, *delta*, *theta*, *phi*, etc.).   Similarly we use d, D for distance, depth or diameter; r, R for radius; l, L for length; w, W for width; h, H for height, etc.

In the following articles are given the solutions of a number of problems which involve right triangles and which utilize the methods outlined above and the fundamental principles studied in Chapters II and IV. In article 32 are given similar problems for solution by the reader in the same general manner.

30. Illustrative Problem Solutions.

Prob. 1. At a horizontal distance of 120 feet from the foot of a steeple, the angle of elevation of the top was found to be $60\frac{1}{2}°$. What is the height of the steeple?

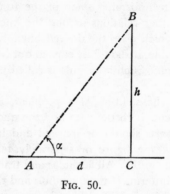

Fig. 50.

Solution.   In Fig. 50 let BC represent the steeple of height h, and A the point from which the top B is observed.   Then AC is the distance d of the observer from the foot of the steeple, AB is the line of sight, and $\angle CAB$ is the angle of elevation, α.   The data are then

$$\alpha = 60° 30', \quad d = 120 \text{ ft.}$$

and h is to be found.

Since the ground is horizontal and the steeple is vertical, $\angle ACB$ is a right angle and hence $h/d = \tan \alpha$.   Solving this for h we have

$$h = d \tan \alpha,$$

which is the *solution formula* for the height h.   Substituting the data, this gives

$$h = 120 \tan 60° 30'.$$

From the tables $\tan 60° 30' = 1.7675$.   Therefore,

$$h = 120 \times 1.7675 = 212.1 \text{ ft.,}$$

the height of the steeple.

Prob. 2.   As viewed from the top of a cliff 326 feet above the level of the water, the angle of depression of a boat is 24°.   How far out from the cliff is the boat?

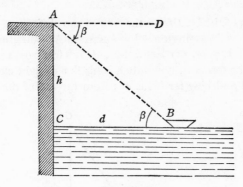

FIG. 51.

Solution.   In Fig. 51, let *AC* represent the vertical face of the cliff and *B* the position of the boat.   Then *BC* = *d* is the distance of the boat from the cliff and *AC* = *h* is the height of the cliff.   *AB* is the line of sight of the observer at *A*, *AD* is the horizontal through *A* and ∠*DAB* is the angle of depression.   Let ∠*DAB* = β.   The data are then

$$h = 326 \text{ ft.,} \quad \beta = 24°,$$

and the distance *d* is to be found.

Taking the line *BC* as horizontal, it is parallel to *AD*, since *AD* is also horizontal.   *AB* is then a transversal cutting two parallels and the angles *DAB*, *ABC* are alternate interior angles.   According to the principle (*F*) of article 5, therefore ∠*ABC* = ∠*DAB*, or ∠*ABC* = β, as shown on the figure.

In the right △*ABC* we have *h/d* = tan β and hence,

$$d = \frac{h}{\tan \beta}.$$

Substituting the data in this solution formula, we get

$$d = \frac{326}{\tan 24°}.$$

From the tables, tan 24° = .4452. Therefore,

$$d = \frac{326}{.4452} = 732 \text{ ft.}$$

is the distance of the boat from the foot of the cliff.

Prob. 3. The Washington Monument in Washington, D. C., is 555 feet high. If a boy five feet tall stands 100 feet from the monument and looks at the top of it, how much is his line of sight elevated above the horizontal and how far is his eye from the top of the monument?

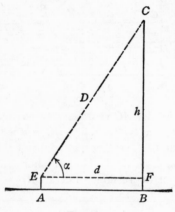

Fig. 52.

Solution. If, in Fig. 52, *BC* represents the monument and *AE* the boy, then *BC* = 555 ft. and *AE* = 5 ft. If we draw *EF* and *AB*, then *EF* is horizontal and *BF* = 5 ft. Hence *h* = *FC* = 550 ft., and also *d* = *EF* = *AB* = 100 ft. The line of sight is then *EC* and the distance of the eye *E* from the top *C* of the monument is *D* = *EC*. The angle of elevation of the line of sight is ∠*FEC* = α.

The data are, therefore,

$$h = 550 \text{ ft.}, \quad d = 100 \text{ ft.},$$

and we have to find α and *D*.

In the right triangle *EFC* we have

$$\tan \alpha = \frac{h}{d} \tag{i}$$

from which the angle α can be found.   With α known, we then have from the same triangle, sin $\alpha = h/D$.   Hence,

$$D = \frac{h}{\sin \alpha}, \qquad \text{(ii)}$$

from which the distance D is found.   Formulas (i) and (ii) are the solution formulas of the problem.

Substituting the data in formula (i) gives

$$\tan \alpha = \tfrac{550}{100} = 5.5000,$$

and, from the tables,

$$\alpha = 79° 42'.$$

Using this value of α and the given value of h in formula (ii),

$$D = \frac{550}{\sin 79° 42'}.$$

From the tables, sin $79° 42' = .9839$.   Therefore,

$$D = \frac{550}{.9839} = 560 \text{ ft.}$$

is the distance from the eye to the top of the monument.

Prob. 4.   At a certain time of the day the elevation of the sun above the horizon is 50° and at that time a tree casts a shadow 80 feet long on level ground.   How high is the tree?

Solution.   In Fig. 53, SA is the direction of the sun's ray to the tip

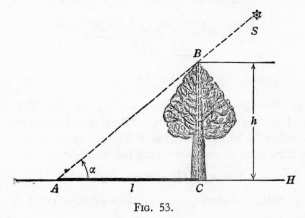

Fig. 53.

of the shadow, $\angle CAS = \alpha$ is the angle of elevation of the sun above the horizon H, and $BC = h$ is the height of the tree. The length of the shadow is then $AC = l$, and h is to be found from the following data:

$$l = 80 \text{ ft.}, \quad \alpha = 50°.$$

In the right triangle ABC, $h/l = \tan \alpha$,

$$\therefore \quad h = l \tan \alpha.$$

Substituting the data this gives,

$$h = 80 \tan 50°,$$

and, from the tables, $\tan 50° = 1.1918$. Therefore,

$$h = 80 \times 1.1918 = 95.34 \text{ ft.}$$

Prob. 5.   The width of a river is determined by a surveyor as follows: At a point A five feet from one bank (Fig. 54) the transit telescope is sighted on a stone B on the other bank directly opposite. The telescope is then turned through the angle $BAC = 90°$ and the line AC laid out. A distance $AC = 100$ feet is then measured off on this line and the transit set up at C. The telescope is next sighted on the original point A and turned through the angle ACB to sight again on the stone at B. This angle is found to be $73° 42'$. What is the width of the river?

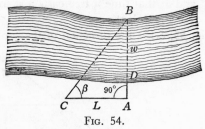

Fig. 54.

Solution. In this method of measurement, the line AC is called a *base line.* Let L represent its length, and let β represent the angle ACB, which is called the *base angle.* If $w = BD$ represents the width of the river, we then have to find w from the following data

$$L = 100 \text{ ft.}, \quad \overline{AD} = 5 \text{ ft.}, \quad \beta = 73° 42'.$$

Since $\triangle ABC$ is a right triangle, we have $\overline{AB}/L = \tan \beta$

$$\therefore \quad \overline{AB} = L \tan \beta.$$

But $\overline{AB} = w + \overline{AD}$, therefore, $w + \overline{AD} = L \tan \beta$,

$$w = L \tan \beta - \overline{AD}.$$

Substituting the data this gives,

$$w = 100 \tan 73° 42' - 5,$$

and, from the tables, $\tan 73° 42' = 3.4197$.   Hence,

$$w = 100 \times 3.4197 - 5 = 341.97 - 5 = 336.97,$$

or,

$$w = 337 \text{ ft.}$$

Prob. 6.   The height of a mountain whose base and summit are inaccessible was determined as follows: On a level plain at some distance from the mountain, the elevation of the summit was read and found to be 30° and at a point one mile farther from the mountain the elevation was again read and found to be 25°.   What is the height?

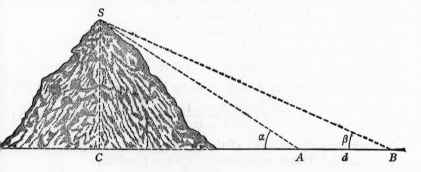

Fig. 55.

Solution.   In Fig. 55, S is the summit of the mountain and $CS = h$ is the height above the level plain BC. At the first observation point, A, the line of sight to the summit is AS and $\angle CAS = \alpha$ is the angle of elevation of S. Similarly, at the second point, B, the elevation is $\angle CBS = \beta$, and the distance between the two points is $AB = d$.

The data of the measurement are, therefore,

$$\alpha = 30°, \quad \beta = 25°, \quad d = 1 \text{ mi.} = 5280 \text{ ft.}$$

and from these the height h is to be found.

In right $\triangle ACS$ the distance AC can be formulated in terms of h and α, and in right $\triangle BCS$ the distance BC can be formulated in terms of h and β.   The distance $d = BC - AC$ and this is known.   When all this is written out we will have a solution formula for h.

In right $\triangle ACS$, $h/\overline{AC} = \tan \alpha$, hence,

$$AC = \frac{h}{\tan \alpha}. \tag{i}$$

Similarly, in right $\triangle BCS$, $h/\overline{BC} = \tan \beta$ and

$$BC = \frac{h}{\tan \beta}. \tag{ii}$$

And as we saw above, $BC - AC = d$.   Using the results (i) and (ii) in this expression for d gives,

$$\frac{h}{\tan \beta} - \frac{h}{\tan \alpha} = d. \tag{iii}$$

In this equation h is the only unknown quantity.   The equation can, therefore, be solved for h in terms of the known quantities, and, from the data, h can then be computed.

In order to solve (iii) for h it may be written as

$$h \cdot \frac{1}{\tan \beta} - h \cdot \frac{1}{\tan \alpha} = d.$$

Hence, taking out h as a common factor in the two terms on the left,

$$h \left(\frac{1}{\tan \beta} - \frac{1}{\tan \alpha} \right) = d. \tag{iv}$$

The common denominator of the two fractions in the parentheses is $\tan \alpha \cdot \tan \beta$.   Therefore, combining the two fractions,

$$h \left(\frac{\tan \alpha - \tan \beta}{\tan \alpha \cdot \tan \beta} \right) = d.$$

Dividing both sides of this equation by the fractional coefficient of h we get finally

$$h = \frac{d \tan \alpha \cdot \tan \beta}{\tan \alpha - \tan \beta}. \tag{v}$$

This is the desired solution formula for the height h, expressing h in terms of the known quantities α, β, d.

Substituting the data in formula (v), we have,

$$h = \frac{5280 \tan 30° \cdot \tan 25°}{\tan 30° - \tan 25°}$$

and, from the tables, tan 30° = .5774, tan 25° = .4663.   Therefore,

$$h = \frac{5280 \times .5774 \times .4663}{.5774 - .4663} = \frac{1420}{.111},$$

$$\therefore \quad h = 12{,}790 \text{ ft.} = 2.42 \text{ mi.}$$

Prob. 7.   An observer in a stationary "captive" balloon at a known height above a level plain in the rear of a front line trench, sights on the trench and finds its angle of depression to be 35°.   He then sights on an enemy machine gun beyond the trench and finds its angle of depression to be 20°.   If the height of the balloon is 2000 feet, how far is the gun from the trench?

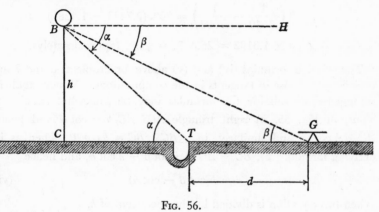

Fig. 56.

Solution.   In Fig. 56, *B* represents the balloon at the end of a cable fastened at *C*, and *BC* = *h* is its height.   *T* is the position of the trench and *G* that of the gun, and *TG* = *d* is the distance of the gun from the trench.   *BH* is the horizontal through *B*.   The angle of depression of the trench is, therefore, $\angle HBT = \alpha$ and that of the gun is $\angle HBG = \beta$.

The data of the problem are,

$$h = 2000 \text{ ft.}, \quad \alpha = 35°, \quad \beta = 20°,$$

and the distance *d* is to be found.

Since *BH* and the plain *CG* are both horizontal they are parallel and, therefore, the alternate angles *HBT* and *CTB* are equal, as are also angles *HBG* and *CGB*.   That is, $\angle CTB = \alpha$, and $\angle CGB = \beta$.

Now the angles *CTB*, *CGB* and the distances *d*, *h*, are related in the same manner in Fig. 56 as in Fig. 55. Therefore, equation (iv) of Prob. 6 holds good in the present case, and

$$d = h \left(\frac{1}{\tan \alpha} - \frac{1}{\tan \beta} \right)$$

is the solution formula for the distance d.

Substituting the data in this formula,

$$d = 2000 \left(\frac{1}{\tan 20°} - \frac{1}{\tan 35°} \right),$$

and from the tables tan 20° = .3640, tan 35° = .7002. Therefore,

$$d = 2000 \left(\frac{1}{.3640} - \frac{1}{.7002} \right) = 2000(2.7473 - 1.4281)$$

$$= 2000 \times 1.3192 = 2639 \text{ ft.} = \tfrac{1}{2} \text{ mi. (approximately).}$$

The solution formulas (iv) and (v) above for Problems 6 and 7 are derived for the use of tangents in the computations. When a table of cotangents is available the formulas may be somewhat simplified. Thus, in Fig. 55, in right triangle ACS $\overline{AC}/h = \cot \alpha$ and hence $\overline{AC} = h \cot \alpha$; and similarly, in $\triangle BCS$, $\overline{BC} = h \cot \beta$. Then as in deriving formula (iii), $\overline{BC} - \overline{AC} = h \cot \beta - h \cot \alpha$, and hence

$$d = h(\cot \beta - \cot \alpha) \qquad \text{(vi)}$$

When this equation is divided by the coefficient of h,

$$h = \frac{d}{\cot \beta - \cot \alpha} \qquad \text{(vii)}$$

These formulas are simpler and easier to use than the corresponding formulas (iv) and (v), when the table of cotangents is available. Thus it is only necessary to read the cotangents of the two given angles and subtract the smaller from the larger. The height h is then multiplied by this difference to find d, or d is divided by the difference to find h.

The cotangents may be found from the table of tangents by remembering that the cotangent of an angle is the tangent of its complement or co-angle. Thus in Prob. 6 cot 30° = tan 60° and cot 25° = tan 65°, and similarly for the angles of Prob. 7.

Prob. 8. A ladder 40 feet long may be so placed that it will just reach a window sill 33 feet above the street level on one side of a street, and by turning it over without moving its foot it will just reach a window sill 21 feet up on the other side.   Find its inclination above the street in each position and find the width of the street.

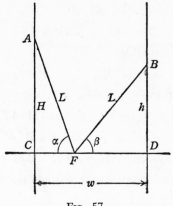

Solution.   In Fig. 57, A is the position of the sill of the higher window on the wall AC and B that of the lower on the wall BD.   Let these heights be H and h respectively.   Then CD is the width w of the street, and if F is the foot of the ladder, FA is one position of the ladder and FB the other.   Let L be the length of the ladder; then $AF = BF = L$.   The inclinations of the ladder in the two positions are the angles $AFC = \alpha$ and $BFD = \beta$.

We have, therefore, as data,

$$L = 40 \text{ ft.}, \quad H = 33 \text{ ft.}, \quad h = 21 \text{ ft.},$$

and are to find α, β and w.

In right $\triangle ACF$ $H/L = \sin \alpha$ and in right $\triangle BFD$, $h/L = \sin \beta$, or,

$$\sin \alpha = \frac{H}{L}, \quad \sin \beta = \frac{h}{L}. \tag{i}$$

Also, in the same triangles, $\overline{CF}/L = \cos \alpha$ and $\overline{FD}/L = \cos \beta$, hence,

$$\overline{CF} = L \cos \alpha, \quad \overline{FD} = L \cos \beta,$$

and the width of the street is $w = CD = CF + FD$.   Therefore,

$$w = L \cos \alpha + L \cos \beta,$$

or,

$$= L(\cos \alpha + \cos \beta). \tag{ii}$$

The formulas (i) give the angles of inclination of the ladder, as H, h, L, are known, and with α, β, thus determined formula (ii) gives the width of the street.

Substituting the data in formulas (i),

$$\sin \alpha = \tfrac{33}{40} = .8250, \quad \sin \beta = \tfrac{21}{40} = .5250,$$

and therefore, from the tables,

$$\alpha = 55° \, 36', \quad \beta = 31° \, 40'.$$

Using these results in formula (ii),

$$w = 40(\cos 55° \, 36' + \cos 31° \, 40'),$$

and from the tables $\cos 55° \, 36' = .5650$, $\cos 31° \, 40' = .8511$.   Hence,

$$w = 40(.5650 + .8511) = 40 \times 1.4161 = 56.64 \text{ ft.}$$

Prob. 9.   To prove (or derive) the formula (viii) of article 4 for the area of a segment of a circle.

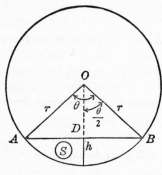

Fig. 58.

Solution.   Figs. 18 and 19 of article 4 are combined in Fig. 58 below, to which reference is now made.   The line OD is perpendicular to the chord AB and bisects angle θ.   In right $\triangle ODB$ therefore $\angle DOB = \tfrac{1}{2}\theta$ and $\overline{OD} = r \cos \left(\tfrac{1}{2}\theta\right)$, $\overline{BD} = r \sin \left(\tfrac{1}{2}\theta\right)$.   The area of the right $\triangle ODB = \tfrac{1}{2}\overline{BD} \cdot \overline{OD}$ and that of the sector $\triangle AOB$ which is twice that of the right triangle is $\triangle AOB = \overline{BD} \cdot \overline{OD}$.   Therefore $\triangle AOB = 2 \times \tfrac{1}{2}r^2 \sin \left(\tfrac{1}{2}\theta\right) \cdot \cos \left(\tfrac{1}{2}\theta\right) = \tfrac{1}{2}r^2[2 \sin \left(\tfrac{1}{2}\theta\right) \cdot \cos \left(\tfrac{1}{2}\theta\right)]$.   Now it is found in article 62, formula (111), that $2 \sin x \cdot \cos x = \sin (2x)$, where x is any angle.   Therefore $2 \sin \left(\tfrac{1}{2}\theta\right) \cdot \cos \left(\tfrac{1}{2}\theta\right) = \sin [2(\tfrac{1}{2}\theta)] = \sin \theta$, and hence the area of

$$\triangle AOB = \tfrac{1}{2}r^2 \sin \theta. \tag{i}$$

It was found in article 4 that the area of the sector AOB is $u = \tfrac{1}{2}r^2\theta$, and it is seen at once from Fig. 58 that the area of the segment is the difference between that of the sector and the triangle, $S = u - \triangle AOB$. Therefore $S = \tfrac{1}{2}r^2\theta - \tfrac{1}{2}r^2 \sin \theta$, and on taking out the common factor $\tfrac{1}{2}r^2$,

$$S = \tfrac{1}{2}r^2(\theta - \sin \theta), \tag{ii}$$

which is the required formula.

By using this formula (ii) the calculation referred to in Example 4, article 4, can now be carried out.

Prob. 10.   If the radius of the tank of Example 4, article 4, is 36 inches and its length is 15 feet, how many gallons of gasoline are in the tank when the liquid is 18 inches deep in the bottom of the tank?

Solution.   Fig. 58 is now an end view of the horizontal tank, with $r = 36$ in. and the depth of the liquid is $h = 18$ in. Therefore $\overline{OD} = r - h = 18$ in., and in $rt\ ODB$, $\cos (\tfrac{1}{2}\theta) = \overline{OD}/r = 18/36 = \tfrac{1}{2}$. Therefore $\tfrac{1}{2}\theta = 60°$ and $\theta = 120° = 2.0944$ radians. Substituting this value in formula (ii) above, with $r = 36$, we get for the cross-section area of the liquid

$$\begin{aligned}
S &= \tfrac{1}{2}(36)^2(2.0944 - \sin 120°) \\
&= \tfrac{1}{2}(1296)(2.0944 - 0.8660) \\
&= 648 \times 1.2284 = 796 \text{ sq. in.}
\end{aligned}$$

The volume of the liquid is the cross-section area multiplied by the length $L = 15$ ft. $= 180$ in.   Therefore

$$V = 796 \times 180 = 143{,}280 \text{ cu. in.}$$

and the number of gallons (231 cu. in. to the gallon) is finally

$$V/231 = 143280 \div 231 = 620.26 \text{ gal.,}$$

or about 620 gal. 1 qt.

31. **Problems in Astronomy.**   If an object is viewed from two positions its direction is different in the two cases.   Thus, if an observer at A in Fig. 59 views an object at P, its direction is AP, or PA.   If the observer moves to B the direction of P is now BP, or PB.   The difference between the two directions PA and PB is the angle APB. This angle is called the *parallax* of P.

If A is one position of the earth in its annual path around the sun S and B its position on the opposite side of the sun six months later (it returns to A again after a year), and P is a stationary heavenly body, say a star, the angle APB is called the *annual parallax* of the star.

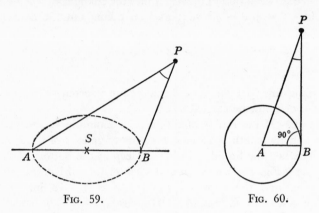

Fig. 59.   Fig. 60.

If A is taken as the center of the earth, as in Fig. 60 (simply for convenience of reference; no observer can reach A), and B on the equator with PB tangent to the earth at B, $\triangle ABP$ is a right triangle and $\angle APB$ is called the *equatorial parallax* of the heavenly body. This is the angle which the earth's semi-diameter would subtend if viewed from the body in question.

Methods of measuring the equatorial and annual parallaxes of heavenly bodies, such as the sun, moon and stars, will be described in a later chapter.

The above definitions of parallax will be utilized in this article in solving some problems of astronomy which involve right triangles. These problems will require no knowledge of astronomy more than the definitions given above, but will illustrate some of the famous applications of trigonometry to astronomy. With the reader's present knowledge of trigonometry these applications will appear surprisingly simple.

Prob. 1. Diameter of the Earth. From the top of a mountain three miles above sea level the angle of depression of the ocean horizon is found to be $2° 13' 50''$. Considering the earth as a sphere, find its diameter.

Solution.   In Fig. 61 (which is not drawn to scale) let the circle with center at O represent the earth and $AB = h$ the height of the mountain. Then BC is the horizontal direction at the top B of the mountain and

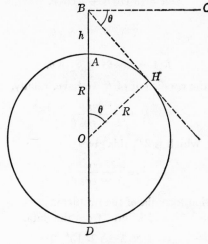

Fig. 61.

H is the horizon. BH is the line of sight to the horizon and $\angle CBH = \theta$ is the angle of depression of H.   The diameter of the earth is $AD = d$ and is twice the radius OA or OH.   We have, therefore,

$$h = 3 \text{ mi.,} \quad \theta = 2° 13' 50'',$$

to find the diameter d.

The line BH just touches the earth's circle at H.   It is, therefore, tangent to the circle at H and is perpendicular to the radius OH.   The triangle OHB is a right triangle and hence $\angle HOB$ is the complement of $\angle HBO$.   But, since $BC \perp OB$, $\angle HBC$ is also the complement of $\angle HBO$.   Therefore $\angle HOB = \theta$, as shown in the figure.

Let R represent the radius of the circle (earth).   Then $OH = OA = R$ and $OB = R + h$.   Also, in the right $\triangle OHB$, $\overline{OH}/\overline{OB} = \cos \theta$ or

$$\overline{OH} = \overline{OB} \cos \theta.$$

Using the values of OH and OB just given, this becomes

$$R = (R + h) \cos \theta,$$

and we have to solve this equation for the radius R. Doubling the radius, we then have the diameter.

Multiplying out the right-hand side of the equation it is

$$R = R \cos \theta + h \cos \theta.$$

Transposing,

$$R - R \cos \theta = h \cos \theta.$$

Factoring,

$$R(1 - \cos \theta) = h \cos \theta.$$

Dividing this by the coefficient of R we have, finally,

$$R = \frac{h \cos \theta}{1 - \cos \theta}.$$

For the diameter, which is $2R$, this gives,

$$d = \frac{2h \cos \theta}{1 - \cos \theta},$$

which is the solution formula of the problem.

Substituting the values of h and θ from the data,

$$d = \frac{2 \times 3 \cos 2° 13' 50''}{1 - \cos 2° 13' 50''}.$$

Using six-place tables we find $\cos 2° 13' 50'' = .999243$. Hence

$$d = \frac{6 \times .999243}{1 - .999243} = \frac{5.995458}{0.000757} = 7920 \text{ miles.}$$

Prob. 2. Distance of the Sun from the Earth. The equatorial parallax of the sun is $8.8''$. Using the diameter of the earth as found above, find the distance from the center of the earth to the center of the sun.

Solution. In Fig. 60 since PB is tangent to the earth's circle at B, $\angle ABP = 90°$ and $\triangle ABP$ is a right triangle. In this right triangle, AB is the radius of the earth, which from Prob. 1 above is 3960 miles. We have, therefore, in Fig. 60,

$$AB = 3960 \text{ mi.,} \quad \angle APB = 0° 0' 8.8'',$$

to find the distance $\overline{AP}$.

In the right $\triangle ABP$, $\overline{AB}/\overline{AP} = \sin \angle APB$. Hence,

$$\overline{AP} = \frac{\overline{AB}}{\sin \angle APB},$$

and on substituting the data,

$$\overline{AP} = \frac{3960}{\sin 8.8''}.$$

To carry out this division accurately it is better to use logarithms as in article 25, and, since the angle is so small, special astronomical tables should be used. The computation is carried out in the usual manner:

$$\log 3960 = 13.5976952 - 10$$
$$-\log \sin 8.8'' = 5.6295869 - 10$$

$$\log (AP) = 7.9681083$$
$$\overline{AP} = 92,919,800 \text{ mi.}$$

The earth-sun distance is, then, about 93 million miles.

Prob. 3.   Diameter of the Sun.   From a point on the earth the sun is sighted with a transit, first on one edge and then on the other, and the angle between the lines of sight is 32′ 4″. Using the earth-sun distance found above, find the diameter of the sun.

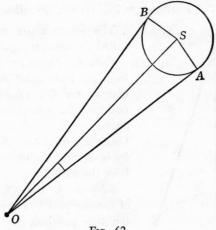

FIG. 62.

Solution.   In Fig. 62 the circle with center at S represents the sun and O is the position of the observer on the earth. OA and OB, which are tangent to the sun, are the lines of sight and $\angle AOB = 32' 4''$. From Prob. 2, above, the distance from the earth's *surface* to the sun's center is (in Fig. 62) $OS = 92,919,800 - 3960$ or about 92,916,000 miles.   The radius of the sun is $SA = SB$ and the diameter is $2\overline{SA}$. The data are, therefore,

$$\overline{OS} = 92,916,000 \text{ mi.,} \quad \angle AOB = 32'\ 4'',$$

and we have to find $2\overline{SA}$.

Since OA is tangent to the circle at A, $\angle OAS = 90°$ and $\triangle OAS$ is a right triangle, with $\angle AOS = \frac{1}{2}(\angle AOB) = 16'\ 2''$. In the right $\triangle OAS$, $\overline{SA}/\overline{OS} = \sin \angle AOS$, hence

$$\overline{SA} = \overline{OS} \sin \angle AOS$$

is our solution formula. Substituting the data,

$$\overline{SA} = 92,916,000 \sin 16'\ 2''.$$

Using the seven-place logarithms for the computation,

$$\begin{aligned}
\log 92916000 &= 7.9680905 \\
+\log \sin 16'\ 2'' &= 7.6687484 - 10 \\
\hline
\log (SA) &= 5.6368389 \\
\overline{SA} &= 433350.
\end{aligned}$$

$\therefore \quad$ Diameter $= 2\overline{SA} = 866,700$ miles.

FIG. 63.

The whole angle AOB, Fig. 62, is called the *apparent angular diameter*.

Prob. 4. *Distance of a Star.* The line from a certain fixed star is perpendicular to the line joining two opposite positions of the earth in its path and the annual parallax of the star is 1.826″. Using the earth-sun distance found in Prob. 2, find the distance of the star from the earth.

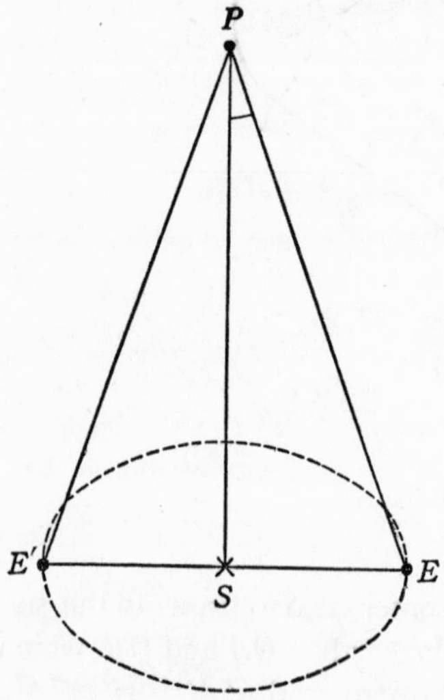

Solution. In Fig. 63, P is the position of the star and S of the sun. E, E' are the two positions of the earth in its path, which is shown as the dotted circle. From Prob. 2 $\overline{ES} = 92,919,800$ mi., and as given, $\angle EPE' = 0°\ 0'\ 1.826''$. With these data, $\overline{EP}$ is to be found.

Since $PS \perp EE'$, $\triangle ESP$ is a right triangle and since $ES = ES'$, $\angle EPS = \angle E'PS = \frac{1}{2}(\angle EPE') = .913''$. Also, in right $\triangle ESP$, $\overline{ES}/\overline{EP} = \sin \angle EPS$.

$$\therefore \quad \overline{EP} = \frac{\overline{ES}}{\sin \angle EPS}.$$

Substituting the data in this solution formula, we have

$$\overline{EP} = \frac{92919800}{\sin .913''}.$$

Performing the computation logarithmically:

$$\log 92919800 = 17.9681083 - 10$$
$$-\log \sin .913'' = 4.6259299 - 10$$

$$\overline{\log (EP) = 13.3421784}$$

$$EP = 21,987,600,000,000 \text{ miles.}$$

This distance is beyond conception. It is also inconvenient to express it in miles. For these reasons it is usual to state such a distance by giving the number of years required by light to travel over it. Light travels at the rate of 186,330 miles per second, so that in one year (365^d 5^h $48'$ $46''$, or $31,556,926''$) it will travel about $5,880,000,000,000$ miles. This distance is called a *light year*.

Dividing the number of miles in one light year into the star distance EP, as found above, we have for the star distance from the earth, in light years,

$$EP = 3.74 \text{ light yr.}$$

The star whose distance we have just calculated is the nearest to the earth. Its name is *Alpha Centauri*. The distances of only a very few stars have been measured. Others are so distant that the annual parallax is too small to measure accurately.

32. Problems for Solution.

1. A monument 200 feet high stands on a level street and the angle of elevation of the top is 3° 30′ at the position of an observer standing on the street. How far is the observer from the monument?

2. A tree 90 feet high casts a shadow 117 feet long. Find the elevation of the sun.

3. From a tower 94 feet high situated on the bank of a river, the angle of depression of the opposite bank is 25° 13′. Find the width of the river.

4. From one edge of an excavation 36 feet wide, the angle of elevation of the top of a wall on the opposite edge is 62° 39′. Find the length of the ladder that will just reach the top of the wall from the point of observation.

5. From a balloon directly above a certain building, the angle of depression of a river eight miles away is 10° 14′. Find the height of the balloon above the level of the river.

6. From a tower 58 feet high, the angles of depression of two objects situated in the same horizontal line with the base of the tower and on the same side, are 30° 13¼′ and 45° 46¼′. Find the distance between the objects.

7. From the top of a hill, the angles of depression of two successive milestones on a straight level road leading to the hill are 15° and 5°. Find the height of the hill.

8. To determine the height of one of the great redwood trees of California, a surveyor lays off a distance of 300 feet from its foot and at the end of the line sets up a transit. He levels the telescope and then sights on the top of the tree. If the angle of elevation is 65° 12′, and the telescope is 5 feet above the level ground, find the height of the tree.

9. The Great Pyramid of Egypt has a square base and symmetrical sloping faces. The inclination of a slanting face is 53° 7′ and at a distance of 600 feet from the base on level ground the angle of elevation of the apex is 27° 9′. Find the vertical *h*eight, *s*lant height, and the *w*idth at the base.

10. The equatorial parallax of the moon is 57′. Using the value of the earth's radius given in Prob. 1, article 31, find the distance of the center of the moon from the center of the earth.

11. The apparent angular diameter of the moon is 31′ 7″. Using the value of its distance from the earth as found in the preceding problem, find its diameter in miles.

12. Telescope observation of the moon shows that when the sun is 38° 40′ above the moon's horizon, the length of the shadow cast by a certain mountain on the moon is 1¼ miles. How high is the mountain?

(NOTE. There are many mountains on the moon nearly four miles high.)

13. The legs of a pair of dividers 5½ inches long are set at an angle of 30° 17′. Determine the distance between the points.

14. From an airplane directly above a town, the angle of depression of another town 18 miles away on level ground was 16°. How far up was the plane when the observation was made?

15. Find the radius of a circle in which a chord 16 feet long subtends an angle of 26° 18′ 14″ at the center.

16. An equilateral triangle is circumscribed about a circle of 21-inch radius. What is the perimeter of the triangle?

17. Derive a formula in terms of radius (r) and central angle (θ) for a chord of a circle.

18. Forty-seven holes are to be drilled at equal distances apart around a circular plate of 21 inches diameter, with their centers each 1½ inches from the edge. Using the formula of Prob. 17 find the distance between centers of successive holes.

19. The horizontal distance between the two extreme positions of the end of a pendulum 27 inches long is 7 inches. Through what angle does the pendulum swing, and how far does the end move in swinging from one extreme position to the other?

20. A ladder 24 feet long is resting against a wall at an angle of 65° 14′ 49″ with a level floor. If the foot of the ladder is drawn 33¾ inches farther away from the wall, how far down the wall will the top move?

21. A girder to carry a bridge is in the form of a circular arc.   The length of the span is 120 feet and the height of the arch is 25 feet.   Find the angle at the center of the circle such that its sides intercept the arc of the girder, and find the radius of the circle.

22. Two observers are stationed a mile apart on a straight east-and-west level road.   An airplane flying north passes over the road between them, and, as it crosses over the road, the angles of elevation are observed to be 72° 30′ and 77° 15′.   Find the height of the plane.

23. A horizontal oil tank 28 feet long and 6 feet in diameter is filled with oil to a depth of 4 feet.   Find the weight of the oil, one cubic foot weighing 50 pounds.

24. A horizontal cylindrical tank, 7 feet in diameter and 25 feet long, is partly filled with water so that the wetted arc of the circumference of the tank is 7.7 feet.   How many gallons are there in the tank, allowing $7\frac{1}{2}$ gallons to the cubic foot?

25. Find the area of the larger of the two segments into which a circle is divided by a chord 25 inches long which is at a distance of 9 inches from the center.

Chapter 6

FUNCTIONS OF ANY ANGLE

33. Introduction. In certain types of problems which involve line and angle measurements, such as those so far considered, it is sufficient to consider only right triangles. This is not always the case, however, and in the problems considered in some of the later chapters it will be necessary to deal with oblique triangles.

Now in right triangles the angles whose functions we use in calculation are always acute angles and so far the tables have only been used for acute angles. In oblique triangles, however, we must make use of obtuse angles. It is necessary, therefore, to study a little more fully the method of representation of angles which was explained in connection with Fig. 7, article 1, and the circle method of representing the functions, Fig. 42, article 14.

We begin with an extension of our ideas on the directions of lines and the sense of generation of angles.

34. Positive and Negative Lines and Angles. From algebra we have the familiar notion of positive and negative numbers and of how operations with negative numbers produce results which are the opposite of the results produced by the corresponding operations with positive numbers. The same ideas are made use of in the representation of directions and angles by means of lines on a diagram.

If any particular point is chosen as a reference or starting point from which measurements may be made or motion may take place in any desired direction, a line or motion in one direction is obviously of a different kind from one in the opposite direction. Also the value of the angle turned through by a generating line in reaching any specified terminal position (Fig. 7), obviously depends on the particular direction chosen for the initial line. Again, with the same initial position the generating line may turn through the same number of degrees in any two cases but the terminal position will depend on the direction or sense of the rotation, and in reaching the same terminal position the number of degrees turned through will in general be different for different directions of rotation.

From these considerations, it is at once obvious that in order to describe lines and angles completely it is necessary to specify five things: the starting point of any line, the length of the line, the angular position of the line with reference to the initial line, the direction in which it is turned from the initial position, and the position of the initial line. All of this is clearly and definitely accomplished in the manner described below in connection with Fig. 64.

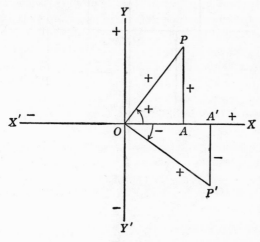

FIG. 64.

The point O in Fig. 64 is chosen as original reference point and is called the *origin*. The horizontal line XX' and the vertical line YY' through O are taken as standard reference lines and are called *axes*. Lines or distances parallel to XX' and on the *right* of YY' are taken as *positive*, those on the *left* are *negative*. Lines or distances parallel to YY' and *above XX'* are *positive*, those *below* are *negative*. The positive horizontal axis OX is taken as the standard *initial line* for all angles. Angles generated in the left-hand or *counter clockwise* direction are *positive* and those in the opposite or *clockwise* direction are *negative*. The terminal line or generating line is sometimes called the *radius vector* and is always taken as *positive* from O outward.

According to this system of reference, OA in Fig. 64 is positive or plus, AP is plus, $A'P'$ is minus, $\angle XOP$ is plus, $\angle XOP'$ is minus, OP and OP' are plus. These are indicated on the diagram.

As the line OP, or OP' rotates about O the position of the end point

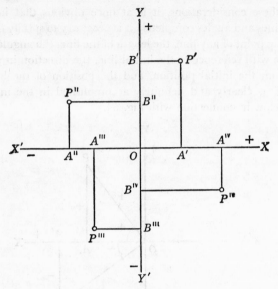

Fig. 65.

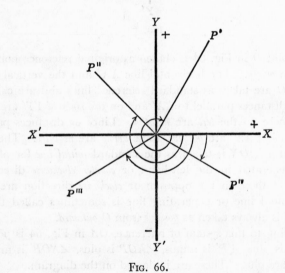

Fig. 66.

P can be specified at any time by stating its distances from XX' and from YY'. These distances are called the *coordinates* of the point. The distance from YY' parallel to XX' is the *abscissa* and the distance from XX' parallel to YY' is the *ordinate* of the point. Thus, in Fig. 64, OA and AP are the coordinates of the point P, OA being its abscissa and AP its ordinate. OA' is the abscissa and $A'P'$ the ordinate of P'. The axis XX' is also called the *axis of abscissas* and YY' the *axis of ordinates*.

The coordinates of a point are positive or negative according to the position of the point. Thus, according to the system of reference we have described, the coordinates of the point P' in Fig. 65 are OA', OB' and both are positive, while those of P''' are OA''', OB''' and both are negative. The coordinates of P'' are OA'', OB'' and the abscissa OA'' is negative while the ordinate OB'' is positive. The coordinates of P^{iv} are OA^{iv}, OB^{iv}; the abscissa OA^{iv} is positive and the ordinate OB^{iv} is negative.

In Fig. 7, article 1, each of the angles BOE, BOF, BOG is positive, as indicated by the arrow heads for $\angle BOE$ and $\angle BOG$. In Fig. 66 each of the angles XOP', XOP'', XOP''', XOP^{iv} is drawn in the negative sense, as indicated. These angles, or any one of them, might also be drawn in the positive sense by rotating the radius vector in the opposite direction, but in that case, each would be a different angle altogether, even though the terminal position of the radius vector would be the same.

The system of reference described and illustrated in this article will now be used as the basis for the definitions of the functions of any angle, acute or obtuse.

35. Functions of Any Angle. In the unit circle of Fig. 42, article 14, the sine of $\angle x$ is the ordinate MP of the point P, the end of the radius vector; the cosine of $\angle x$ is the abscissa OM and the tangent of $\angle x$ is the length of the tangent line from the positive axis of abscissas to the terminal line OP produced. The cotangent of $\angle x$ is the tangent of the complement of x, that is, the tangent line from the positive axis of ordinates to the radius vector OP produced.

Since we now have the means of measuring and specifying positive and negative coordinates, tangent lines and angles, we can extend the circular definitions of the functions of angles to apply to *angles in any quadrant*, not restricting our consideration to the first quadrant as in Fig. 42. This is done as shown in Figs. 67, 68, 69.

In each case in these diagrams the circle is the *unit circle* (radius vector = 1), the initial line is OA, the terminal line is OP and the angle x is $\angle AOP$. The functions of the angle x in any quadrant are then defined as follows:

$$\sin x = PM = \textit{ordinate of } P,$$
$$\cos x = OM = \textit{abscissa of } P.$$
$$\tan x = AT = \textit{tangent from positive axis of abscissas}$$
$$\text{to radius vector } OP \text{ produced.}$$

These are shown for all four quadrants in Figs. 42, 67, 68, 69.

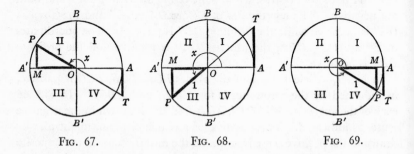

FIG. 67.   FIG. 68.   FIG. 69.

36. Signs and Values of Functions of Angles in Each Quadrant.

From the rules for signs of coordinates in the various quadrants we see from Fig. 67 that in the second quadrant the sine is positive, while the cosine and tangent are negative. From Fig. 68 the sine and cosine are negative in the third quadrant, while the tangent is positive. In the fourth quadrant, from Fig. 69, the cosine is positive and the sine and tangent are negative. We recall from article 16 that in the first quadrant all three of the chief functions are positive.

In these diagrams the cotangent is not shown, but it is in each case the tangent line from the point B to the terminal line OP produced (forward or backward). The reader can easily draw the one or two lines showing the cotangent in each case.

The length of the radius vector being always 1 in the unit circle, the magnitude and sign of each function can also be found by means of the ordinary right triangle definition applied to each quadrant, and for later purposes this interpretation will be very useful. Thus, in Fig. 42 we have in the first quadrant, according to the rules of signs, in the right $\triangle MOP$:

$$\sin x = \frac{+\overline{PM}}{+\overline{OP}} = \frac{+\overline{PM}}{+1} = +\overline{PM},$$

$$\cos x = \frac{+\overline{OM}}{+\overline{OP}} = \frac{+\overline{OM}}{+1} = +\overline{OM},$$

$$\tan x = \frac{+\overline{AT}}{+\overline{OA}} = \frac{+\overline{AT}}{+1} = +\overline{AT}.$$

Similarly, in the second quadrant, right $\triangle MOP$, Fig. 67:

$$\sin x = \frac{+\overline{PM}}{+\overline{OP}} = \frac{+\overline{PM}}{+1} = +\overline{PM},$$

$$\cos x = \frac{-\overline{OM}}{+\overline{OP}} = \frac{-\overline{OM}}{+1} = -\overline{OM},$$

$$\tan x = \frac{+\overline{PM}}{-\overline{OM}} = \frac{-\overline{AT}}{+\overline{OA}} = \frac{-\overline{AT}}{1} = -\overline{AT}.$$

In the same way the value and sign of each of the functions can be found from Figs. 68, 69 for the third and fourth quadrants.

It is to be noted that in the last equation above we can write $(+\overline{PM})/(-\overline{OM}) = (-\overline{AT})/(+\overline{OA})$ because the vertical angles MOP and AOT are equal and the right triangles PMO and TAO are similar. Therefore, according to (Q), article 6, the ratios of the corresponding sides are equal. The same principle applies in the other figures.

According to the principle just referred to, the values of the right triangle ratios do not depend on the lengths of the separate sides but only on the angle. Therefore, in Figs. 42, 67, 68, 69 the *ratios do not depend on the length of the radius vector OP* but only on the angle. We may then use the coordinates of the point P of *any* radius vector OP, as in Fig. 65, when we wish to represent the functions by means of the right triangle *ratios*. The unit circle with radius vector equal to 1 is used only when we wish to represent the values of the functions by the *lengths* of the coordinates and tangent line.

In Fig. 65, the abscissa $B'P' = OA'$, $B''P'' = OA''$, etc., and it is not necessary to show $B'P'$, $B''P''$, etc. Fig. 65 may be drawn as Fig. 70, the abscissas being OA', OA'', etc. In Fig. 70, are shown also the radius vectors OP', OP'', etc.

According to the preceding paragraphs, and taking into account the

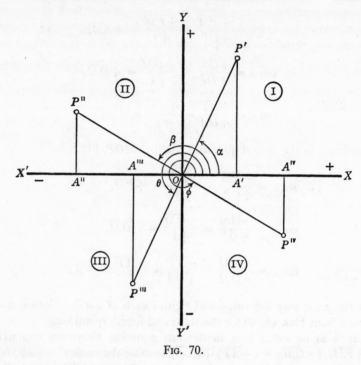

FIG. 70.

signs of the various coordinates, we have in the various quadrants in Fig. 70 the following results:

I. $\sin \alpha = +\dfrac{\overline{A'P'}}{\overline{OP'}}$ $\cos \alpha = +\dfrac{\overline{OA'}}{\overline{OP'}}$ $\tan \alpha = +\dfrac{\overline{A'P'}}{\overline{OA'}}$

II. $\sin \beta = +\dfrac{\overline{A''P''}}{\overline{OP''}}$ $\cos \beta = -\dfrac{\overline{OA''}}{\overline{OP''}}$ $\tan \beta = -\dfrac{\overline{A''P''}}{\overline{OA''}}$

III. $\sin \theta = -\dfrac{\overline{A'''P'''}}{\overline{OP'''}}$ $\cos \theta = -\dfrac{\overline{OA'''}}{\overline{OP'''}}$ $\tan \theta = +\dfrac{\overline{A'''P'''}}{\overline{OA'''}}$

IV. $\sin \phi = -\dfrac{\overline{A^{iv}P^{iv}}}{\overline{OP^{iv}}}$ $\cos \phi = +\dfrac{\overline{OA^{iv}}}{\overline{OP^{iv}}}$ $\tan \phi = -\dfrac{\overline{A^{iv}P^{iv}}}{\overline{OA^{iv}}}$

Following along the line in this list for each quadrant we see at once the sign of the functions in that quadrant. Following down the column for each function we can follow its changes in sign from quadrant to quadrant. These results are concisely shown in Table III, the sign of the cotangent being determined from the ratios as above or from the relation $\cot x = \dfrac{\cos x}{\sin x}$, the sine and cosine being given their proper signs and the sign of the cotangent being the algebraic sign of the quotient.

TABLE III

Quad. Funct.	I	II	III	IV
sine..........	+	+	−	−
cosine........	+	−	−	+
tangent.......	+	−	+	−
cotangent.....	+	−	+	−

If in Figs. 42, 67, 68, 69, we follow the generating line OP as it passes through all the quadrants of the unit circle and note the values of the functions by means of the lengths of the lines PM, OM, AT we see that when OP lies on OA', $MP = 0$, $OM = OA' = -1$, and $AT = 0$. But $\angle AOA' = 180°$. Therefore, when $x = 180°$, $\sin x = 0$, $\cos x = -1$, $\tan x = 0$. Similarly, when $x = 270°$ OP lies on OB' and

TABLE IV

Angle Funct.	0°	90°	180°	270°	360°
sine..........	0	+1	0	−1	0
cosine........	+1	0	−1	0	+1
tangent........	0	∞	0	∞	0
cotangent......	∞	0	∞	0	∞

we have $MP = OB' = -1$, $OM = 0$, and AT becomes infinitely long, or $AT = \infty$. That is, when $x = 270°$, $\sin x = -1$, $\cos x = 0$, $\tan x = \infty$. In the same way, when OP again reaches the initial position OA, $x = 360°$ and the functions are the same as for $x = 0°$, which have already been found in article 15, as have those for 90°. These results are all collected in Table IV, where in each case $\cot = 1/\tan$.

Tables III and IV should be committed to memory.

37. How to Read Functions of Obtuse Angles in the Tables. Let us consider Fig. 70 a little further. A portion of this figure is given below as Fig. 71.

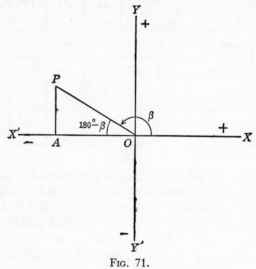

FIG. 71.

In Fig. 71 $\angle XOP = \beta$ and as in Fig. 70

$$+\frac{\overline{AP}}{\overline{OP}} = \sin\beta, \quad -\frac{\overline{OA}}{\overline{OP}} = \cos\beta, \quad -\frac{\overline{AP}}{\overline{OA}} = \tan\beta.$$

But, from the original right triangle definitions we have in the right triangle OAP, since $\angle AOP$ is less than 90°,

$$+\frac{\overline{AP}}{\overline{OP}} = \sin\angle AOP, \quad +\frac{\overline{OA}}{\overline{OP}} = \cos\angle AOP, \quad +\frac{\overline{AP}}{\overline{OA}} = \tan\angle AOP,$$

and also, $\angle AOP = 180° - \beta$. Therefore,

$$\left.\begin{array}{rl} \sin \beta = & \sin (180° - \beta), \\ \cos \beta = & -\cos (180° - \beta), \\ \tan \beta = & -\tan (180° - \beta). \end{array}\right\} \quad (26)$$

and similarly for the other functions.

Now, β is any angle between 90° and 180°. Also, in Fig. 70, $\alpha = 180° - \angle X'OP'$ and since α is less than 90°, $\angle X'OP'$ is between 90° and 180° and the same relations hold for $\angle X'OP'$ and α as for β and $\angle AOP$, respectively. In general, therefore, the formulas (26) may be expressed in words as follows:

Corresponding functions of supplementary angles are equal and the sines have the same sign.

This means that any function of an angle between 90° and 180° is numerically the same as that given in the table for the supplement of that angle. It must be remembered, however, that the cosine and tangent are negative while the sine is positive. From these results we have the following

RULE. *To read functions of angles between 90° and 180° in the tables, subtract the angle from 180° and take from the tables the same function of the remainder. Before the cosine and tangent thus obtained place a minus sign.*

Using this rule we find from the table,

$$\sin 120° = \sin (180° - 120°) = \sin 60° = .8660,$$

$$\cos 120° = -\sin (180° - 120°) = -\cos 60° = - .5000,$$

$$\tan 120° = -\tan (180° - 120°) = -\tan 60° = -1.7321.$$

Similarly

$$\sin 135° = \sin 45° = .7071,$$

$$\cos 135° = -\cos 45° = - .7071,$$

$$\tan 135° = -\tan 45° = -1.0000,$$

$$\sin 116° 33' = .8945,$$

$$\cos 116° 33' = - .4470,$$

$$\tan 116° 33' = -2.0013.$$

The results of this and the preceding articles will be of frequent use in following chapters.

38. Exercises.

By the use of the method of the preceding article read from the tables the sine, cosine and tangent of the angles given in the chart below and write them in the spaces indicated, with the proper sign.

Angle	sine		cosine		tangent	
	Sign	Value	Sign	Value	Sign	Value
97° 18′..........						
164° 48′.........						
140° 10′.........						
100° 0′..........						
99° 19½′.........						
178° 30′.........						
91° 24¼′.........						
179° 59′.........						
165° 2.3′........						

Chapter 7

PROPERTIES AND FORMULAS
OF OBLIQUE TRIANGLES

39. The Sine Law. By a *law* in mathematics is meant a statement or relation which always holds good under the same specified conditions, or a relation (usually expressed as a formula or equation) which certain variables always satisfy or obey. We proceed to develop such a relation between the sides of a triangle and the sines of its angles.

In Fig. 72 or 73, let ABC represent any *oblique* triangle (C is *not* a right angle) with sides a, b, c, respectively, opposite the angles A, B, C and draw in either triangle the altitude $CD \perp AB$.

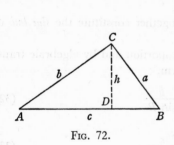

FIG. 72.

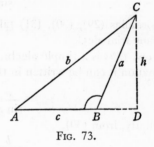

FIG. 73.

In either figure, triangles ADC and BDC are right triangles and in right $\triangle ADC$ we have

$$\sin A = \frac{h}{b}. \tag{27}$$

In Fig. 72 in right $\triangle BDC$,

$$\sin B = \frac{h}{a} \tag{28}$$

and in Fig. 73 in right $\triangle BDC$, $\sin \angle DBC = h/a$. But $\angle B$ and $\angle DBC$ are supplementary and, therefore, $\sin B = \sin \angle DBC$. Therefore,

$$\sin B = \frac{h}{a},$$

99

which is the same as (28). Relations (27) and (28) hold, therefore, in any form of oblique triangle, whether the altitude falls inside or outside the triangle.

Dividing equation (27) by (28) we obtain,

$$\frac{\sin A}{\sin B} = \frac{\left(\dfrac{h}{b}\right)}{\left(\dfrac{h}{a}\right)} = \frac{h}{b} \cdot \frac{a}{h},$$

$$\therefore \quad \frac{\sin A}{\sin B} = \frac{a}{b}. \tag{29}$$

By drawing the altitude in either triangle through A and B in turn we would get, in the same way,

$$\frac{\sin B}{\sin C} = \frac{b}{c}, \tag{30}$$

$$\frac{\sin A}{\sin C} = \frac{a}{c}. \tag{31}$$

Formulas (29), (30), (31) taken together constitute the *sine law* of oblique triangles.

Now, (29) is a simple algebraic proportion and by algebraic transformation it can be written in the form,

$$\frac{a}{\sin A} = \frac{b}{\sin B}. \tag{32}$$

Similarly, from (30),

$$\frac{b}{\sin B} = \frac{c}{\sin C}, \tag{33}$$

and, on comparing this with (32), it is seen at once that (32) and (33) can be written as a continued proportion with the three ratios:

$$\frac{a}{\sin A} = \frac{b}{\sin B} = \frac{c}{\sin C}, \tag{34}$$

and this also includes (31), which, separately, can be written

$$\frac{a}{\sin A} = \frac{c}{\sin C}.$$

Forms (29), (30), (31) are for some types of calculation more useful than the combined form (34), but (34) is the most easily remembered form of statement of the sine law, and any two of its ratios taken together give (29), (30), or (31).

From (34) we have the following statement of the

SINE LAW: *In any triangle the sides are proportional to the sines of the opposite angles.*

If, in (29), (30) or (31), any one angle is a right angle, its sine is equal to 1 and the opposite side is the hypotenuse, and the formula becomes simply the right triangle formula for the sine. Therefore, the sine law holds good for *either* right or oblique triangles, while the original function formulas are restricted to right triangles *only*.

40. The Cosine Law. In Fig. 72 or 73 in the right $\triangle ADC$,

$$\frac{h}{b} = \sin A, \quad \frac{\overline{AD}}{b} = \cos A.$$

$$\therefore \quad h = b \sin A, \tag{35}$$

$$\overline{AD} = b \cos A.$$

In Fig. 72,

$$d = c - \overline{AD}.$$

In Fig. 73,

$$d = \overline{AD} - c.$$

$$\left. \begin{array}{l} \therefore \quad d = c - b \cos A, \\[4pt] d = b \cos A - c. \end{array} \right\} \tag{36}$$

or

In either right triangle BCD, $a^2 = h^2 + d^2$, hence, using (35), (36),

$$a^2 = (b \sin A)^2 + (c - b \cos A)^2,$$

or

$$a^2 = (b \sin A)^2 + (b \cos A - c)^2.$$

But

$$(c - b \cos A)^2 = (b \cos A - c)^2 = b^2 \cos^2 A - 2bc \cos A + c^2.$$

$$\therefore \quad a^2 = b^2 \sin^2 A + b^2 \cos^2 A - 2bc \cos A + c^2,$$

$$= b^2(\sin^2 A + \cos^2 A) + c^2 - 2bc \cos A.$$

But by equation (16), article 8, $\sin^2 A + \cos^2 A = 1$. Therefore,

$$a^2 = b^2 + c^2 - 2bc \cos A. \tag{37}$$

Similarly, by taking b and c in turn we get,

$$b^2 = c^2 + a^2 - 2ca \cos B, \tag{38}$$

$$c^2 = a^2 + b^2 - 2ab \cos C. \tag{39}$$

In (37) it is to be noted that A is the angle included between sides b and c and that a is the side opposite angle A. Similarly, in (38) and (39) B, c, a and C, a, b, respectively, are related in the same way.

Formulas (37), (38), (39) constitute the *cosine law* of oblique triangles. In either case, if the angle is 90°, its cosine is zero and the product term vanishes, and the opposite side is the hypotenuse. The formula then becomes the hypotenuse-square law of the right triangle. Therefore, the formulas apply also to the right triangle. They may, therefore, be stated in words as follows:

COSINE LAW: *In any triangle the square of any side equals the sum of the squares of the other two sides, minus twice their product times the cosine of their included angle.*

If the included angle in any case is between 90° and 180°, its cosine is negative and the product term in the formula is to be added.

By transposing equation (37) and dividing by the coefficient of cos A it may be transformed into

$$\cos A = \frac{b^2 + c^2 - a^2}{2bc}. \tag{40}$$

Similarly,

$$\cos B = \frac{c^2 + a^2 - b^2}{2ca}. \tag{41}$$

$$\cos C = \frac{a^2 + b^2 - c^2}{2ab}. \tag{42}$$

These forms of the cosine law are frequently useful.

41. The Tangent Law. According to formula (29)

$$\frac{a}{b} = \frac{\sin A}{\sin B}.$$

This is an ordinary algebraic proportion of the form $a/b = c/d$ and in algebra we learn that by the transformation called *composition and division* this can be written $\dfrac{a + b}{a - b} = \dfrac{c + d}{c - d}$. The sine proportion can, therefore, be written

$$\frac{a + b}{a - b} = \frac{\sin A + \sin B}{\sin A - \sin B}. \tag{43}$$

Now, according to formula (129), article 64, we have,

$$\frac{\sin A + \sin B}{\sin A - \sin B} = \frac{\tan \frac{1}{2}(A + B)}{\tan \frac{1}{2}(A - B)}.$$

Comparing this formula with (43) we see at once that

$$\frac{a+b}{a-b} = \frac{\tan \frac{1}{2}(A+B)}{\tan \frac{1}{2}(A-B)}. \tag{44}$$

Similarly,

$$\frac{b+c}{b-c} = \frac{\tan \frac{1}{2}(B+C)}{\tan \frac{1}{2}(B-C)}. \tag{45}$$

$$\frac{c+a}{c-a} = \frac{\tan \frac{1}{2}(C+A)}{\tan \frac{1}{2}(C-A)}. \tag{46}$$

These three formulas constitute the *tangent law* of oblique triangles. Since it is derived from the sine law which holds good for both right and oblique triangles, we can, therefore, state it in words as follows:

TANGENT LAW: *In any triangle the sum of any two sides is to their difference as the tangent of half the sum of the opposite angles is to the tangent of half their difference.*

In any particular case of formulas (44), (45), (46), the side b may be greater than a, c greater than b, or a greater than c. In any case, the larger side and angle are written first, and the smaller second, in the numerators and denominators of the formulas.

By a simple transformation, each of the tangent law formulas can be put into a form which is useful in the solution of triangles. Thus, if (44) is multiplied by $\tan \frac{1}{2}(A-B)$ and by $\dfrac{a-b}{a+b}$ it becomes

$$\tan \tfrac{1}{2}(A-B) = \frac{(a-b) \tan \frac{1}{2}(A+B)}{a+b}. \tag{47}$$

Similarly,

$$\tan \tfrac{1}{2}(B-C) = \frac{(b-c) \tan \frac{1}{2}(B+C)}{b+c}. \tag{48}$$

$$\tan \tfrac{1}{2}(C-A) = \frac{(c-a) \tan \frac{1}{2}(C+A)}{c+a}. \tag{49}$$

42. The Segment Law. In Fig. 74, let c be the longest side of the oblique triangle ABC and b the shortest, and draw the altitude h on

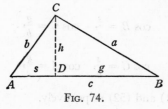

FIG. 74.

the side c as base. Let g be the greater segment BD of side c, and s the smaller segment AD.

In right $\triangle BDC$, $\qquad\qquad\qquad g^2 = a^2 - h^2$.

In right $\triangle ADC$, $\qquad\qquad\qquad s^2 = b^2 - h^2$.

Subtracting, $\qquad\qquad\qquad\qquad g^2 - s^2 = a^2 - b^2$.

Factoring this, $\qquad (g + s)(g - s) = (a + b)(a - b)$.

$$\therefore \quad g - s = \frac{(a + b)(a - b)}{g + s}.$$

But from the figure

$$g + s = c, \quad \therefore \quad g - s = \frac{(a + b)(a - b)}{c}. \tag{50}$$

Similarly,

$$g + s = a, \quad g - s = \frac{(b + c)(b - c)}{a}, \tag{51}$$

$$g + s = b, \quad g - s = \frac{(c + a)(c - a)}{b}, \tag{52}$$

when a and b, respectively, are the longest sides. In either of the formulas the longer of the other two sides in the numerator is written first in every case.

The formulas (50), (51), (52) constitute the *segment law* of triangles. In words it is:

SEGMENT LAW: *In any triangle the altitude drawn to the longest side divides that side into segments whose sum is that side, and whose difference is the product of the sum and difference of the other two sides, divided by that side.*

If the three sides a, b, c of a triangle are known, the segments g and s are given by solving the appropriate pair of equations (50), (51) or (52). With g and s known we then have from the right triangles in Fig. 74, corresponding to formula (50),

$$\cos A = \frac{s}{b}, \quad \cos B = \frac{g}{a} \tag{53}$$

Similarly,

$$\cos B = \frac{s}{c}, \quad \cos C = \frac{g}{b}, \tag{54}$$

$$\cos C = \frac{s}{a}, \quad \cos A = \frac{g}{c}, \tag{55}$$

corresponding to (51) and (52) respectively.

In each of these three pairs of formulas, it is to be noted that the segment g is adjacent to the greater of the two sides other than the base, and s is adjacent to the smaller. In using g and s to find the two angles adjacent to the base it is, therefore, necessary to be careful that the angles and sides are not confused. It is always best to draw a figure.

43. Area of an Oblique Triangle. According to the principle (L), article 5, the area of any triangle is half the product of its base and altitude, and we have seen in article 27 how this principle can be used to express the area of a right triangle in terms of its various parts. The same can be done in the case of an oblique triangle and there are as many formulas for the area as there are combinations of three or more parts of the triangle. We shall develop here only a few of the most useful.

Any side of a triangle may be taken as base and the triangle will, therefore, have three altitudes. If we take the side c as base, for example, the triangle may be represented by Fig. 75 and $CD = h$ is the altitude. The area K is then

$$K = \tfrac{1}{2}ch. \tag{56}$$

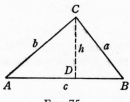

Fig. 75.

If the side b and $\angle A$ are known, then in the right triangle ADC, $h/b = \sin A$, or

$$h = b \sin A.$$

This value of h when used in formula (56) gives for the area

$$K = \tfrac{1}{2}bc \sin A. \tag{57}$$

Now, A is the angle included between the sides b and c, and a similar formula could in the same way be obtained for a, c, B or a, b, C. We have, therefore, this result:

The area of any triangle equals half the product of any two of its sides times the sine of their included angle.

If, instead of two sides and their included angle, there are known two angles and their included side (or, a side and the two adjacent angles) formula (57) can be transformed so as to express K in terms of these.

Thus, suppose A, B, c known. Then, by the sine law,

$$\frac{b}{c} = \frac{\sin B}{\sin C},$$

$$b = c \left(\frac{\sin B}{\sin C}\right). \tag{58}$$

But, $\sin C = \sin (180° - C)$ and $180° - C = A + B$; therefore,

$$\sin C = \sin (A + B).$$

Putting this value of $\sin C$ in formula (58), it becomes,

$$b = c \frac{\sin B}{\sin (A + B)}.$$

Putting this value of b in (57), we have, finally,

$$K = \frac{c^2 \sin A \cdot \sin B}{2 \sin (A + B)}, \tag{59}$$

with corresponding formulas for B, C, a and A, C, b.

Therefore, *the area of a triangle equals half the square of any side times the product of the sines of the adjacent angles, divided by the sine of the sum of those angles.*

By the "sine of the sum of two angles," as $\sin (A + B)$, is meant the sine of that number of degrees found by adding the two angles. Thus, if $A = 17° 43'$, $B = 27° 17'$, $\sin (A + B) = \sin 45° = .7071$.

Another very useful formula gives the area in terms of the three sides. While the formula itself is simple, its derivation is somewhat long and complicated. We shall, therefore, not give all the details of the derivation but shall give only the main steps in the derivation.

Since for any angle, say A, $\sin^2 A + \cos^2 A = 1$, then $\sin^2 A = 1 - \cos^2 A$ and, therefore,

$$\sin A = \sqrt{1 - \cos^2 A}.$$

Using this value of $\sin A$ in formula (57) we get for the area

$$K = \tfrac{1}{2}bc\sqrt{1 - \cos^2 A}. \tag{60}$$

Now, by the cosine law, formula (40), article 40,

$$\cos A = \frac{b^2 + c^2 - a^2}{2bc}.$$

and this value of cos A when used in (60) gives for the area

$$K = \tfrac{1}{2}bc \sqrt{1 - \left(\frac{b^2 + c^2 - a^2}{2bc}\right)^2},$$

and this formula contains only the three sides of the triangle. In order to render it suitable for easy computation, however, it must be transformed into a somewhat different form.

Since

$$\left(\frac{b^2 + c^2 - a^2}{2bc}\right)^2 = \frac{(b^2 + c^2 - a^2)^2}{4b^2c^2},$$

then

$$K = \tfrac{1}{2}bc \sqrt{1 - \frac{(b^2 + c^2 - a^2)^2}{4b^2c^2}} = \tfrac{1}{2}bc \sqrt{\frac{4b^2c^2 - (b^2 + c^2 - a^2)^2}{4b^2c^2}}.$$

Removing $4b^2c^2$ from the denominator under the radical the bc on the outside cancels and

$$K = \tfrac{1}{4}\sqrt{4b^2c^2 - (b^2 + c^2 - a^2)^2}. \tag{61a}$$

Now $4b^2c^2 = (2bc)^2$ and the expression under the radical in (61a) is the difference of two squares. Such a difference may be factored, as $A^2 - B^2 = [A - B] \cdot [A - B]$, and therefore the expression under the radical becomes

$$(2bc)^2 - (b^2 + c^2 - a^2)^2$$
$$= [(2bc) + (b^2 + c^2 - a^2)] \cdot [(2bc) - (b^2 + c^2 - a^2)]$$
$$= [(b^2 + 2bc + c^2) - a^2] \cdot [a^2 - (b^2 - 2bc + c^2)]$$
$$= [(b + c)^2 - a^2] \cdot [a^2 - (b - c)^2]$$
$$= [(b + c + a)(b + c - a)] \cdot [(a + b - c)(a - (b - c))]$$
$$= (a + b + c)(-a + b + c)(a - b + c)(a + b - c).$$

Writing this form of the expression under the radical in (61a) we get

$$K = \tfrac{1}{4}\sqrt{(a + b + c)(-a + b + c)(a - b + c)(a + b - c)}. \tag{61b}$$

If now we let s represent half the sum of the sides (not the smaller segment, s, in article 42), that is,

$$s = \tfrac{1}{2}(a + b + c),$$

then,

$$a + b + c = 2s$$
$$-a + b + c = 2s - 2a = 2(s - a),$$
$$a - b + c = 2s - 2b = 2(s - b),$$
$$a + b - c = 2s - 2c = 2(s - c),$$

and these values substituted in ($61b$) give,

$$K = \tfrac{1}{4}\sqrt{2s \cdot 2(s - a) \cdot 2(s - b) \cdot 2(s - c)}.$$

Simplifying this we have, finally, for the area

$$
\left.
\begin{aligned}
K &= \sqrt{s(s - a)(s - b)(s - c)} \\
s &= \tfrac{1}{2}(a + b + c).
\end{aligned}
\right\}
\tag{62}
$$

with

To find the area, therefore, when the three sides are known, we have simply to *find half the sum of the sides and from this number subtract separately each side; the square root of the product of the remainders by the half sum is the area.*

In each of the formulas of this article, all the sides must be expressed in the same unit. The area is then expressed in the corresponding unit of square measure.

Chapter 8

OBLIQUE TRIANGLE CALCULATIONS

44. Solution of Oblique Triangles. As in the case of a right triangle, an oblique triangle is said to be *solved* when all its parts not originally known are found by any process from those parts which are known. In the right triangle, one of the six parts is fixed and always known so that only two need be independently given in order to solve the triangle. Thus, three parts must be known. Similarly, in order to solve an oblique triangle three parts must be known and at least one of the three must be a side. (If three angles are given the shape of the triangle is determined, but it may still have any size and so is not completely determined.) Since there is no part of an oblique triangle which retains always the same value, as in the case of the right triangle, all three of the given parts must be independently specified in each case.

The solution of an oblique triangle by calculation is carried out by means of the formulas developed in the preceding chapter, and as in the case of the right triangle, the selection of the appropriate formulas for each computation will depend on the parts that are given. Thus, if any two sides and their included angle are given, the corresponding form of the cosine law or the tangent law may be used. If any two angles and a side opposite one of them, or any two sides and an angle opposite one of them are given, the sine law may be used. If all three sides are given, either the segment law or the second form of the cosine law may be used.

In any particular case, it may be more convenient to begin the solution by the use of the formula or formulas appropriate to that case and after one or two parts are found, to complete the solution by using another formula or set of formulas. In every case, it is to be remembered that the sum of the three angles of the triangle equals 180 degrees.

By examining the various formulas of the triangle and summarizing the discussion of this article we obtain the results set forth in Table V.

In Case II, it is to be noted that before the sine law can be applied,

TABLE V

Case	Given	Law to Use
I	2 ∠s and side opp one	Sine
II	1 side and 2 adj ∠s	Sine
III	2 sides and ∠ opp one	Sine
IV	2 sides and included ∠	Cosine Tangent
V	3 sides	Segment Cosine

the third angle must be found by subtracting from 180° the sum of the two given angles. In Cases III and IV, it will generally be found that after one or two parts are found, the solution is very simply completed by the use of the appropriate sine law formula. In any case, when two angles have been given or found, the third can be found by subtracting their sum from 180°. It serves as a check, however, to find the third angle independently by means of the sine law.

The necessary calculations may be carried out by means of the natural functions and direct computation, either by the use of the slide rule or by arithmetic, or by means of the logarithmic functions and logarithmic computation. Both these methods are illustrated in this chapter for each case of Table V.

In reading either the natural or the logarithmic functions from the tables the method of article 37 is to be used for obtuse angles. In simple triangle solutions, however, where the direction of a line or of an angle does not matter, the plus sign may be used in all cases.

45. Illustrative Examples. Direct Solution.

Case I. Given two angles and a side opposite one of them: A, B, b (Fig. 76).

Given:	To find:
$A = 79° 59'$	$C = 55° 20'$
$B = 44° 41'$	$a = 795$
$b = 568$	$c = 664$

Formulas: $C = 180° - (A + B);\ a = \dfrac{b \sin A}{\sin B};\ c = b \dfrac{\sin C}{\sin B}.$

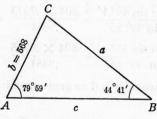

FIG. 76.

CALCULATION

$$A + B = 124° 40',\quad C = 180° - 124° 40' = 55° 20'.$$

$$a = \frac{568 \sin 79° 59'}{\sin 44° 41'} = \frac{568 \times .9848}{.7032} = 795.$$

$$c = \frac{568 \sin 55° 20'}{\sin 44° 41'} = \frac{568 \times .8225}{.7032} = 664.$$

Case II.   Given, one side and the two adjacent angles: *a, B, C* (Fig. 77).

Given:	*To find:*
$a = 804$	$A = 99° 55'$
$B = 45° 1'$	$b = 577$
$C = 35° 4'$	$c = 469$

Formulas: $A = 180° - (B + C);\ b = \dfrac{a \sin B}{\sin A};\ c = \dfrac{a \sin C}{\sin A}.$

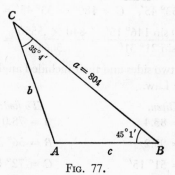

FIG. 77.

Calculation

$$B + C = 80° 5'; \quad A = 180° - 80° 5' = 99° 55'.$$

$$b = \frac{804 \sin 45° 1'}{\sin 99° 55'} = \frac{804 \times .7073}{.9851} = 577.$$

$$c = \frac{804 \sin 35° 4'}{\sin 99° 55'} = \frac{804 \times .5745}{.9851} = 469.$$

Case III.   Given, two sides and an angle opposite one of them: a, b, A (Fig. 78).

Given:	To find:
$a = 840$	$B = 12° 14'$
$b = 485$	$C = 146° 15'$
$A = 21° 31'$	$c = 1272$

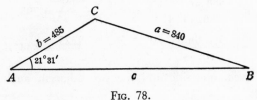

Fig. 78.

Formulas: $\sin B = \dfrac{b \sin A}{a}$; $C = 180° - (A + B)$; $c = \dfrac{a \sin C}{\sin A}$.

Calculation

$$\sin B = \frac{485 \sin 21° 31'}{840} = \frac{485 \times .3668}{840} = .2119, \quad \therefore \quad B = 12° 14'.$$

$$A + B = 33° 45', \quad C = 180° - 33° 45' = 146° 15'.$$

$$c = \frac{840 \sin 146° 15'}{\sin 21° 31'} = \frac{840 \times .5556}{.3668} = 1272.$$

Case IV.   Given, two sides and their included angle: b, c, A (Fig. 79).
1st Solution: Cosine Law.

Given:	To find:
$b = 83.4$	$a = 78.0$
$c = 95.2$	$B = 56° 31'$
$A = 51° 15'$	$C = 72° 14'$

Formulas:

$$a^2 = b^2 + c^2 - 2bc \cos A; \quad \sin B = \frac{b \sin A}{a}; \quad C = 180° - (A + B).$$

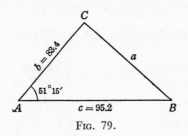

Fig. 79.

CALCULATION

$$a^2 = (83.4)^2 + (95.2)^2 - (2 \times 83.4 \times 95.2) \cos 51° 15'$$
$$= (6950 + 9080) - (15880 \times .6259) = 16030 - 9940 = 6090,$$
$$\therefore \quad a = \sqrt{6090} = 78.0.$$

$$\sin B = \frac{83.4 \sin 51° 15'}{78.0} = \frac{83.4 \times .7799}{78.0} = .8340, \quad \therefore \quad B = 56° 31'.$$

$$A + B = 107° 46', \quad C = 180° - 107° 46' = 72° 14'.$$

For logarithmic computation, the tangent law is more suitable.

Case IV.   2nd Solution: Tangent Law.

Formulas:

$$\tfrac{1}{2}(C + B) = \tfrac{1}{2}(180° - A); \quad \tan \tfrac{1}{2}(C - B) = \frac{(c - b) \tan \tfrac{1}{2}(C + B)}{c + b};$$
$$C = \tfrac{1}{2}(C + B) + \tfrac{1}{2}(C - B); \quad B = \tfrac{1}{2}(C + B) - \tfrac{1}{2}(C - B); \quad a = \frac{b \sin A}{\sin B}.$$

CALCULATION

$$\tfrac{1}{2}(C + B) = \tfrac{1}{2}(180° - 51° 15') = \tfrac{1}{2}(128° 45') = 64° 22\tfrac{1}{2}',$$
$$c + b = 178.6, \quad c - b = 11.8.$$

$$\tan \tfrac{1}{2}(C - B) = \frac{11.8 \tan 64° 22\tfrac{1}{2}'}{178.6} = \frac{11.8 \times 2.0848}{178.6} = .1378,$$
$$\therefore \quad \tfrac{1}{2}(C - B) = 7° 51\tfrac{1}{2}',$$

$$C = 64° 22\tfrac{1}{2}' + 7° 51\tfrac{1}{2}' = 72° 14',$$

$$B = 64° 22\tfrac{1}{2}' - 7° 51\tfrac{1}{2}' = 56° 31'.$$

$$a = \frac{83.4 \sin 51° 15'}{\sin 56° 31'} = \frac{83.4 \times .7799}{.8340} = 78.0.$$

Case V. Given, the three sides: *a*, *b*, *c* (Fig. 80).   1st Solution: Segment Law.

Given:	To find:
$a = 73$	$A = 49° 35'$
$b = 82$	$B = 58° 47'$
$c = 91$	$C = 71° 38'$

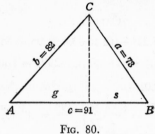

Fig. 80.

Formulas:

$$g - s = \frac{(b + a)(b - a)}{c}; \quad g + s = c;$$

$$g = \tfrac{1}{2}[(g + s) + (g - s)]; \quad s = c - g;$$

$$\cos A = \frac{g}{b}; \quad \cos B = \frac{s}{a}; \quad C = 180° - (A + B).$$

CALCULATION

$$b + a = 155, \quad b - a = 9, \quad g - s = \frac{155 \times 9}{91} = 15.34, \quad g + s = 91,$$

$$g = \tfrac{1}{2}(91 + 15.34) = 53.17, \quad s = 91 - 53.17 = 37.83.$$

$$\cos A = \frac{53.17}{82} = .6483, \quad \therefore \quad A = 49° 35'.$$

$$\cos B = \frac{37.83}{73} = .5183, \quad \therefore \quad B = 58° 47'.$$

$$A + B = 108° 22', \quad C = 180° - 108° 22' = 71° 38'.$$

Case V.   2nd Solution: Cosine Law.

Formulas:

$$\cos A = \frac{b^2 + c^2 - a^2}{2bc}; \quad \sin B = \frac{b \sin A}{a}; \quad C = 180° - (A + B).$$

CALCULATION

$$\cos A = \frac{(82)^2 + (91)^2 - (73)^2}{2 \times 82 \times 91} = \frac{6720 + 8280 - 5330}{164 \times 91} = \frac{9670}{164 \times 91}$$

$$= .6483, \quad \therefore \quad A = 49° 35'.$$

$$\sin B = \frac{82 \sin 49° 35'}{73} = \frac{82 \times .7613}{73} = .8552, \quad B = 58° 47'.$$

$$A + B = 108° 22', \quad C = 180° - 108° 22' = 71° 38'.$$

For logarithmic computation, the segment law is more suitable.

46. Illustrative Examples.   Logarithmic Solution.

Case I.   Given, two angles and the side opposite one: B, C, c,

Given:	*To find:*	*Formulas:*
$B = 40° 8'$	$A = 100° 10'$	$A = 180° - (B + C)$
$C = 39° 42'$	$a = 730.0$	$a = \dfrac{c \sin A}{\sin C}$
$c = 473.7$	$b = 489.2$	$b = \dfrac{c \sin B}{\sin C}$

COMPUTATION

$$B + C = 79° 50', \quad A = 180° - 79° 50' = 100° 10'.$$

$\log 473.7 = \quad 2.6755$	$\log 473.7 = \quad 2.6755$
$+\log \sin 100° 10' = \quad 9.9931 - 10$	$+\log \sin 40° 8' = \quad 9.8093 - 10$
$\log \text{Prod.} = 12.6686 - 10$	$\log \text{Prod.} = 12.4848 - 10$
$-\log \sin 39° 42' = \quad 9.8053 - 10$	$-\log \sin 39° 42' = \quad 9.8053 - 10$
$\log a = \quad 2.8633$	$\log b = \quad 2.6795$
$a = 730.0$	$b = 478.1$

Case II.   Given, one side and the two adjacent angles: b, A, C.

Given:	*To find:*	*Formulas:*
$b = 647.2$	$B = 41°\,42'$	$B = 180° - (A + C)$
$A = 104°\,7'$	$a = 943.4$	$a = \dfrac{b \sin A}{\sin B}$
$C = 34°\,11'$	$c = 546.5$	$c = \dfrac{b \sin C}{\sin B}$

COMPUTATION

$$A + C = 138°\,18', \quad B = 180° - 138°\,18' = 41°\,42'$$

log 647.2 = 2.8110	log 647.2 = 2.8110
+log sin 104° 7′ = 9.9867 − 10	+log sin 34° 11′ = 9.7496 − 10
log Prod. = 12.7977 − 10	log Prod. = 12.5606 − 10
−log sin 41° 42′ = 9.8230 − 10	−log sin 41° 42′ = 9.8230 − 10
log a = 2.9747	log c = 2.7376
$a = 943.4$	$c = 546.5$

Case III.   Given, two sides and the angle opposite one: b, c, B

Given:	*To find:*	*Formulas:*
$b = 10.47$	$C = 7°\,10'$	$\sin C = \dfrac{c \sin B}{b}$
$c = 1.432$	$A = 58°\,40'$	$A = 180° - (B + C)$
$B = 114°\,10'$	$a = 9.800$	$a = \dfrac{b \sin A}{\sin B}$

COMPUTATION

log 1.432 = 0.1559	log 10.47 = 1.0199
+log sin 114° 10′ = 9.9602 − 10	+log sin 58° 40′ = 9.9315 − 10
log Prod. = 10.1161 − 10	log Prod. = 10.9514 − 10
−log 10.47 = 1.0199	−log sin 114° 10′ = 9.9602 − 10
log sin C = 9.0962 − 10	log a = 0.9912
$C = 7°\,10'$	$a = 9.800$

$$B + C = 121°\,20', \quad A = 180° - 121°\,20' = 58°\,40'.$$

Case IV.   Given, two sides and their included angle: a, b, C.   (Tangent Law.)

Given:	To find:	Formulas:

$a = 1004$ $A = 40° 47'$ $\frac{1}{2}(A + B) = \frac{1}{2}(180° - C)$

$b = 943.7$ $B = 37° 53'$ $\tan \frac{1}{2}(A - B) = \dfrac{(a - b) \tan \frac{1}{2}(A + B)}{a + b}$

$C = 101° 20'$ $c = 1507.$

$A = \frac{1}{2}(A + B) + \frac{1}{2}(A - B)$
$B = \frac{1}{2}(A + B) - \frac{1}{2}(A - B)$

$$c = \frac{a \sin C}{\sin A}$$

COMPUTATION

$$\tfrac{1}{2}(A + B) = \tfrac{1}{2}(180° - 101° 20') = 39° 20';$$
$$a - b = 60.3; \quad a + b = 1947.7.$$

$\log 60.3 = \quad 1.7803$	$\log 1004 = \quad 3.0017$
$+\log \tan 39° 20' = \quad 9.9135 - 10$	$+\log \sin 101° 20' = \quad 9.9914 - 10$
$\log \text{Prod.} = 11.6938 - 10$	$\log \text{Prod.} = 12.9931 - 10$
$-\log 1947.7 = \quad 3.2895$	$-\log \sin 40° 47' = \quad 9.8150 - 10$
$\log \tan \frac{1}{2}(A - B) = \quad 8.4043 - 10$	$\log c = \quad 3.1781$

$\frac{1}{2}(A - B) = \quad 1° 27'$
$\frac{1}{2}(A + B) = 39° 20'$

$A = 40° 47'$
$B = 37° 53'$

$c = 1507$

Case V.   Given, the three sides: a, b, c.   (Segment Law.)

Given:	To find:
$a = 37.46$	$A = 53° 5'$
$b = 43.99$	$B = 110° 13'$
$c = 13.50$	$C = 16° 42'$

Formulas:

$$g + s = b; \quad g - s = \frac{(a + c)(a - c)}{b}$$

$$g = \tfrac{1}{2}[(g + s) + (g - s)]; \quad s = \tfrac{1}{2}[(g + s) - (g - s)]$$

$$\cos A = \frac{s}{c}; \quad \cos C = \frac{g}{a}; \quad B = 180° - (A + C).$$

COMPUTATION

$$g + s = 43.99, \quad a + c = 50.96, \quad a - c = 23.96.$$

log 50.96 = 1.7072	log 8.11 = 10.9090 − 10
+log 23.96 = 1.3797	−log 13.50 = 1.1303
log Prod. = 3.0869	log cos A = 9.7787 − 10
−log 43.99 = 1.6434	
log (g − s) = 1.4435	A = 53° 5′

g − s = 27.77	log 35.88 = 11.5549 − 10
g + s = 43.99	−log 37.46 = 1.5736
2g = 71.76	log cos C = 9.9813 − 10
2s = 16.22	
	C = 16° 42′

$$g = 35.88$$
$$s = 8.11$$

$$A + C = 69° 47', \quad B = 180° - 69° 47' = 110° 13'.$$

47. Illustrative Examples.   Areas.

1. *Given:* Two sides and their included angle.

Formula: $K = \frac{1}{2}bc \sin A$.

Direct Calculation: $b = 17.5, c = 21.6, A = 43° 14'$.

$$K = \tfrac{1}{2}(17.5 \times 21.6) \sin 43° 14' = 17.5 \times 10.8 \times .6850 = 129.5.$$

Logarithmic: $a = 123.4, b = 98.7, C = 27° 19'$.

$$\log 123.4 = 2.0913$$
$$+\log 98.7 = 1.9943$$
$$+\log \sin 27° 19' = 9.6618 - 10$$
$$\overline{\log \text{Prod.} = 3.7474}$$
$$\text{Prod.} = 5590$$
$$K = \tfrac{1}{2}(\text{Prod.}) = 2795.$$

2. *Given:* One side and the two adjacent angles.

Formula: $K = \dfrac{1}{2} \dfrac{c^2 \sin A \sin B}{\sin (A + B)}$.

Direct Calculation: c = 73.5, A = 18° 17′, B = 59° 21′.

$$K = \frac{(73.5)^2}{2} \frac{\sin 18°17′ \cdot \sin 59° 21′}{\sin 77° 38′} = 2700\left(\frac{.3137 \times .8603}{.9768}\right) = 745.$$

Logarithmic: b = 418.3, A = 24° 32′, C = 62° 13′, A + C = 86° 45′.

$$\log 418.3 = \quad 2.6215$$

$$\begin{aligned}
\log (418.3^2) = \quad & 5.2430 \\
+\log \sin 24° 32′ = \quad & 9.6183 - 10 \\
+\log \sin 62° 13′ = \quad & 9.9468 - 10 \\
\hline
\log \text{Prod.} = \quad & 14.8081 - 10 \\
-\log \sin 86° 45′ = \quad & 9.9993 - 10 \\
\hline
\log \text{Quot.} = \quad & 4.8088 \\
\text{Quot.} = \quad & 64388
\end{aligned}$$

$$K = \tfrac{1}{2}(\text{Quot.}) = 32{,}194.$$

3. *Given:* The three sides.

Formulas: $s = \tfrac{1}{2}(a + b + c)$, $K = \sqrt{s(s - a)(s - b)(s - c)}$.

Direct Calculation: a = 12, b = 15, c = 18.

$s = \tfrac{1}{2}(12 + 15 + 18) = 22.5$, $s - a = 10.5$, $s - b = 7.5$, $s - c = 4.5$.

$$K = \sqrt{22.5 \times 10.5 \times 7.5 \times 4.5} = \sqrt{8000} = 89.5.$$

Logarithmic: a = 123.4, b = 234.5, c = 345.6,

$$s = \tfrac{1}{2}(123.4 + 234.4 + 345.6) = 351.7,$$

$$s - a = 228.4, \quad s - b = 117.3, \quad s - c = 6.2$$

$$\begin{aligned}
\log 351.8 = & \ 2.5462 \\
+\log 228.4 = & \ 2.3587 \\
+\log 117.3 = & \ 2.0693 \\
+\log \quad 6.2 = & \ 0.7924 \\
\hline
\log \text{Prod.} = & \ 7.7666
\end{aligned}$$

$$\tfrac{1}{2}(\log \text{Prod.}) = \log K = 3.8833$$

$$K = 7643.7.$$

48. Exercises in Oblique Triangles.

Solve the following twelve triangles by the use of the natural functions and direct calculation, computing the sides to three figures and the angles to the nearest minute.

1. $a = 50$
   $A = 10°$
   $B = 46° 36'$

2. $a = 28$
   $b = 34$
   $C = 49°$

3. $b = 999$
   $A = 37° 58'$
   $C = 65° 2'$

4. $a = 14$
   $b = 17$
   $c = 9$

5. $b = 87.9$
   $c = 49.8$
   $A = 33° 10'$

6. $a = 64.1$
   $A = 70° 55'$
   $C = 52° 9'$

7. $a = 80.4$
   $A = 99° 55'$
   $B = 45° 1'$

8. $a = 312$
   $c = 129$
   $B = 124° 40'$

9. $a = 78$
   $b = 101$
   $c = 29$

10. $a = 641$
    $b = 529$
    $c = 702$

11. $b = 96$
    $c = 46.5$
    $C = 29°$

12. $a = 79.5$
    $A = 79° 59'$
    $B = 44° 41'$

Solve the following twelve triangles by the use of logarithmic functions and logarithmic computation:

13. $a = .7293$
    $b = .6850$
    $C = 139° 6.7'$

14. $a = 5.684$
    $b = 8.432$
    $c = 4.212$

15. $b = 872.5$
    $c = 632.7$
    $A = 80°$

16. $a = 9.399$
    $b = 9.197$
    $A = 120° 35'$

17. $b = 13.57$
    $B = 13° 57'$
    $C = 57° 13'$

18. $a = 6412$
    $A = 70° 55'$
    $C = 52° 9'$

19. $A = 78° 19'$
    $B = 54° 27'$
    $c = 1005$

20. $b = 43.99$
    $c = 13.50$
    $B = 110° 13'$

21. $a = 6.342$
    $b = 7.295$
    $c = 8.418$

22. $a = 77.99$
    $b = 83.39$
    $C = 72° 15'$

23. $a = 5968$
    $c = 7034$
    $B = 39° 27'$

24. $a = 65.43$
    $b = 58.26$
    $c = 49.23$

Find the areas of the following triangles, by direct or logarithmic computation, as may be best adapted to the data:

25. $a = 12.38$
    $b = 6.78$
    $C = 46° 24'$

26. $A = 76° 38'$
    $C = 40° 5'$
    $b = 100$

27. $a = 49.00$
    $b = 50.25$
    $c = 25.69$

28. $b = 15.36$
    $c = 11.46$
    $A = 47° 30'$

29. $A = 17° 43'$
    $B = 101° 41'$
    $c = 3.436$

30. $a = 63.89$
    $b = 138.2$
    $c = 121.2$

Answers are given for the last six exercises in areas. The reader who requires further practice and desires to rely on his own results should compute the areas of other triangles from among the first twenty-four exercises of this list.

Chapter 9

SOLUTION OF PROBLEMS
INVOLVING OBLIQUE TRIANGLES

49. Introduction. In the solution of problems involving oblique triangles, as in the case of right triangles, a figure should always be drawn, not necessarily to scale but indicating the positions and relations of the known and required lines and angles. Additional lines may then be drawn as aids in formulating the relations between the known and required parts. The values of the known parts should then be tabulated or written on the figure, and the required parts should also be listed or indicated.

From the various laws of the oblique triangle, formulas can then usually be selected which will express each required part in terms of the known parts; this formula is the required *solution formula* of the problem. It may be that in certain cases the solution formula is not obtained directly, but only after certain algebraic combinations or transformations have been performed. In such cases, symbols should be used in the transformations and the result or results reduced to the simplest form in every case before the numerical computation is begun. The computation should then be carried out by the most appropriate and convenient method.

50. Illustrative Problem Solutions. *Prob.* 1. In Prob. 9, article 32, find the slant height of the pyramid by means of a single oblique triangle calculation.

Solution. In Fig. 81, *ABC* represents the pyramid, with base *BC*,

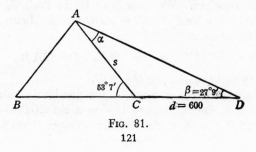

Fig. 81.

121

apex A and slant height $AC = s$. The angles $ACB = 53°\ 7'$ and $ADC = 27°\ 9'$ and the distance $CD = d = 600$ ft. are given, and, in the oblique triangle ACD, we have to find the side AC.

Let $\triangle CAD = \alpha$ and $\triangle CDA = \beta$. Then, $\alpha = 180° - (\beta + \triangle ACD)$. But $\triangle ACD = 180° - 53°\ 7'$. Hence, $\alpha = 180° - (27°\ 9' + 180° - 53°\ 7') = 25°\ 58'$. We have, therefore,

$$\alpha = 25°\ 58', \quad \beta = 27°\ 9', \quad d = 600 \text{ ft.,}$$

to find s.

In oblique $\triangle ACD$, $s/\sin \beta = d/\sin \alpha$. Therefore,

$$s = \frac{d \sin \beta}{\sin \alpha},$$

is the solution formula of the problem.

Substituting in this formula the data given above,

$$s = \frac{600 \sin 27°\ 9'}{\sin 25°\ 58'} = \frac{600 \times .4563}{.4378} = 625 \text{ ft.}$$

Prob. 2. In Prob. 6, article 32, find the distance of the observer from the farther of the two objects, using the answer to that problem as part of the data.

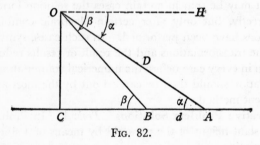

Fig. 82.

Solution. In Fig. 82, let A and B represent the objects and O the position of the observer. We then have (as in Prob. 7, article 30) $\angle OAB = \angle HOA = \alpha$ and $\angle OBC = \angle HOB = \beta$. Letting $AB = d$, the data are, therefore,

$$\alpha = 30°\ 13\tfrac{1}{4}', \quad \beta = 54°\ 46\tfrac{1}{4}', \quad d = 43.1 \text{ ft.,}$$

and we have to find the distance $OA = D$.

In the oblique $\triangle OAB$, we have, by the sine law, $D/\sin \angle OBA = d/\sin \angle AOB$. But, since $\angle OBA = 180° - \beta$, $\sin \angle OBA = \sin \beta$. If we let $\theta = \angle AOB$, therefore, the formula becomes $D/\sin \beta = d/\sin \theta$.

$$\therefore \quad D = \frac{d \sin \beta}{\sin \theta}.$$

From the figure, $\theta = \beta - \alpha = 15° 33'$. The complete data are, therefore,

$$d = 43.1 \text{ ft.}, \quad \beta = 45° 46\tfrac{1}{4}', \quad \theta = 15° 33'.$$

$$\therefore \quad D = \frac{43.1 \sin 45° 46\tfrac{1}{4}'}{\sin 15° 33'} = \frac{43.1 \times .7166}{.2681} = 115.1 \text{ ft.}$$

Prob. 3.   A fort with vertical walls is situated at the top of a smoothly sloping hill. The distance along the slope from an attacking gun to the foot of the wall has been found (by the method of a previous problem) to be 600 feet and the inclination of the hillside to be 47°. The angle of elevation of the top of the wall above the hillside is 8° 40'. Find the distance of the top of the wall from the attacking gun, and the height of the wall.

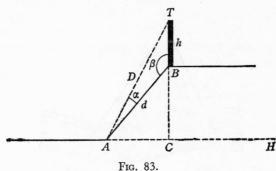

FIG. 83.

Solution.   The situation is indicated in Fig. 83. AB represents the hillside, BT is the wall of the fort, A is the position of the gun, and AH is the horizontal.

We then have $\angle HAB = 47°$, distance to base of wall $AB = 600$ feet, $\angle BAT = 8° 40'$, and are to find the height of the wall BT and the distance of the gun from the top AT.

In Fig. 83, draw the vertical line BC. Then, in the right triangle ABC, since $\angle BAC = 47°$, $\angle ABC = 43°$. Hence, $\angle ABT = 180° - \angle ABC = 137°$. If we let this angle be β, $\angle BAT = \alpha$, and the height $BT = h$, distance $AB = d$, $AT = D$, we have for the data in oblique $\triangle ABT$,

$$\alpha = 8° 40', \quad \beta = 137°, \quad d = 600 \text{ ft.,}$$

and are to find h and D.

By the sine law in oblique $\triangle ABT$, $h/\sin \alpha = d/\sin \angle ATB$, and $\angle ATB = 180° - (\alpha + \beta) = 34° 20'$. Therefore,

$$h = \frac{600 \sin 8° 40'}{\sin 34° 20'} = \frac{600 \times .1507}{.5640} = 160.4 \text{ ft.}$$

Also, in the same triangle, $D/\sin \beta = d/\sin \angle ATB$, or,

$$D = \frac{d \sin \beta}{\sin \angle ATB}.$$

$$\therefore \quad D = \frac{600 \sin 137°}{\sin 34° 20'} = \frac{600 \times .6820}{.5640} = 726 \text{ ft.}$$

Prob. 4. In order to determine the distance of a rock in a lake (A, Fig. 84) from a point (B) on the shore, a line is laid off along the

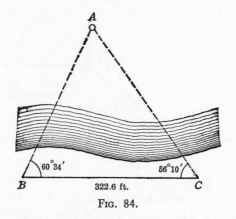

FIG. 84.

shore from that point to another point (C) a measured distance away. The rock is sighted with the transit from both ends of this line and each end of the line is sighted from the other end. In this way, the angles CBA and BCA are measured. If $\angle CBA = 60° 34'$, $\angle BCA = 56° 10'$ and the line $BC = 322.6$ feet, find the required distance AB.

Solution. The measuring scheme is indicated in the figure (Fig. 84) and it is seen at once that it forms the oblique $\triangle ABC$, in which the two angles at B and C with their adjacent or included side BC are known, and the single side AB is required.

By the sine law, $\overline{AB}/\sin C = \overline{BC}/\sin A$.   Therefore,

$$\overline{AB} = \frac{\overline{BC}\sin C}{\sin A}. \qquad (i)$$

Now, $\angle C$ and side BC are given but $\angle A$ is not. A is easily found, however, since $A = 180° - (B + C)$ and both B and C are known. Using the given values of B and C, $A = 180° - 116° 44' = 63° 16'$. The data are, therefore,

$$A = 63° 16', \quad C = 56° 10', \quad \overline{BC} = 322.6 \text{ ft.}$$

Using these values in the solution formula (i), we have

$$\overline{AB} = \frac{322.6 \sin 56° 10'}{\sin 63° 16'} = \frac{322.6 \times .8307}{.8931} = 300 \text{ ft.}$$

NOTE.   The line BC is called a *base line*, as in Prob. 5, article 30, but it is here not necessary to make the angle at either end of the base line equal to exactly 90°.   Thus, with the oblique triangle formulas the line may be run in any convenient position and the angles at both ends may have any values. Such lines are much used in surveying, as will be seen in the next article.

Prob. 5.   Two military observers five miles apart on a level plain and facing each other, find that the angles of elevation of an observation balloon above the line joining them are 55 and 58 degrees, respectively. Find the distance of the balloon from each observer and its height above the plain.

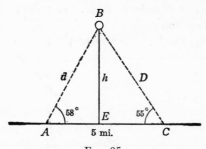

FIG. 85.

Solution.   In Fig. 85, let B represent the balloon, BE its anchoring cable and A, C the positions of the observers on the plain AC.   The data are then as indicated on the figure and we have to find the distances $AB = d$, $CB = D$ and the height $EB = h$.

If we let $\angle ABC = B$, then $B = 180° - (\angle B + \angle C) = 180° - 113°$

= 67°. In the oblique $\triangle ABC$ by the sine law $d/\sin C = \overline{AC}/\sin B$, hence

$$d = \frac{\overline{AC}\sin C}{\sin B}. \tag{i}$$

Similarly,

$$D = \frac{\overline{AC}\sin A}{\sin B}. \tag{ii}$$

With d known from formula (i), then in right $\triangle AEB$, $h/d = \sin A$. Hence

$$h = d\sin A. \tag{iii}$$

Formulas (i), (ii), (iii) are the solution formulas of the problem and the data are:

$$A = 58°, \quad B = 67°, \quad C = 55°, \quad AC = 5 \text{ mi.}$$

Carrying out the calculations,

$$d = \frac{5\sin 55°}{\sin 67°} = \frac{5 \times .8192}{.9205} = 4.45 \text{ mi.}$$

$$D = \frac{5\sin 58°}{\sin 67°} = \frac{5 \times .8480}{.9205} = 4.61 \text{ mi.}$$

$$h = 4.45\sin 58° = 4.45 \times .8480 = 3.77 \text{ mi.}$$

Prob. 6. Two trains start at the same time from the same station and move along straight tracks that form an angle of 30°, one travelling at 30 and the other at 40 miles an hour. How far apart are the trains at the end of half an hour?

Solution. In Fig. 86, let A represent the station and AB, AC the

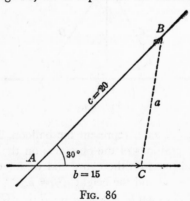

Fig. 86

tracks, making the angle at $A = 30°$.   If, then, B represents the position at the end of the half hour of the 40-mile train, and C that of the 30-mile train, we have $AB = c = 20$ mi., $AC = b = 15$ mi., and are to find the distance $BC = a$.

In the oblique $\triangle ABC$ we have given the two sides b, c, and their included angle A, to find the side a opposite A.   Using the cosine law we have for the solution formula,

$$a^2 = b^2 + c^2 - 2bc \cos A,$$

and substituting in this the data, we get

$$a^2 = (15)^2 + (20)^2 - 2 \times 15 \times 20 \cos 30°,$$

$$= 225 + 400 - 600 \times .8660 = 625 - 519.6 = 105.4.$$

$$\therefore \quad a = \sqrt{105.4} = 10.26, \text{ or about } 10\tfrac{1}{4} \text{ mi.}$$

Prob. 7.   Two towns are 15 miles apart and one is due east of the other.   A third town is 10 miles from the second in a general northeasterly direction and 14 miles from the first in a general northwesterly direction.   Find its exact direction from each of the first two.

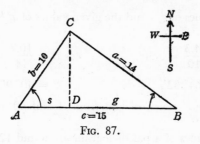

Fig. 87.

Solution. If, in Fig. 87, A, B represent the positions of the first two towns and C the third, then $\overrightarrow{AB}$ is the west-east direction and we have to find the angles BAC, ABC with the distances $AB = 15$, $AC = 10$, $BC = 14$ miles as the data.   If these distances are represented, respectively, by c, b, a the data are as indicated in the figure and the angles to be found are A, B.

Draw the altitude CD on AB as base and let the segments into which it divides AB be g, s as indicated.   Then, according to the segment law of oblique triangles we have,

$$g + s = c, \quad g - s = \frac{(a + b)(a - b)}{c}, \tag{i}$$

and with g, s known from these formulas we have in the right triangles CDA, CDB,

$$\cos A = \frac{s}{b}, \quad \cos B = \frac{g}{a}, \tag{ii}$$

The four formulas (i), (ii) are the solution formulas of the problem, the data being the values of the sides a, b, c shown in the figure.

Substituting the data in the second of formulas (i),

$$g - s = \frac{(14 + 10)(14 - 10)}{15} = \frac{24 \times 4}{15} = 6.4.$$

Using the given value of c in the first of formulas (i) we then have the two equations to solve for g and s:

$$g + s = 15$$
$$g - s = 6.4$$

Adding, $2g = 21.4$

Subtracting, $2s = 8.6$

$$\therefore \quad g = 10.7, \quad s = 4.3 \text{ mi.}$$

Using these values of g, s and the given values of a, b in the formulas (ii) we have,

$$\cos A = \frac{4.3}{10} = .4300, \qquad \cos B = \frac{10.7}{14} = .7643;$$

$$\therefore \quad A = 64° 32', \qquad\qquad B = 40° 9'.$$

That is, C is 64° 32' north of east from A and 40° 6' north of west from B.

Prob. 8.   The sides of a parallelogram are 6 and 12 inches and the acute angles made by the sides are 60 degrees.   Find the diagonals.

Solution.   In Fig. 88, $ABCD$ is the parallelogram, the sides and angles being indicated as given.   The diagonals BC, AD are to be found.

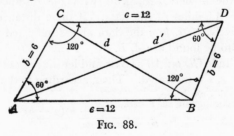

Fig. 88.

Since the opposite sides are parallel, the acute and obtuse angles are supplementary (article 5); therefore, $\angle ABD = 120°$.

The diagonal $BC = d$ is the third side of the oblique $\triangle ABC$ of which the two sides $AB = c = 12$, $AC = b = 6$, and their included angle $BAC = A = 60°$ are known. Therefore, by the cosine law

$$d^2 = b^2 + c^2 - 2bc \cos A. \tag{i}$$

Similarly, in oblique $\triangle ABD$, $AB = c$, $BD = b$, $\angle ABD = B = 120°$ and the diagonal $AD = d'$ is given by

$$d'^2 = b^2 + c^2 - 2bc \cos B.$$

But $B = 120°$ is an obtuse angle, and $\cos B = -\cos (180° - B) = -\cos A$. Therefore,

$$d'^2 = b^2 + c^2 + 2bc \cos A. \tag{ii}$$

The formulas (i) and (ii) are the same except for the signs before the last term. The two diagonals of a parallelogram are, therefore, given by the single formula

$$d^2 = b^2 + c^2 \pm 2bc \cos A, \tag{iii}$$

where b, c are the sides and A is their included *acute* angle. The plus sign gives the long diagonal and the minus sign the short one.

Using the given data in formula (iii) we have,

$$d^2 = 6^2 + 12^2 \pm 2 \times 6 \times 12 \cos 60° = 36 + 144 \pm 144 \times \tfrac{1}{2},$$

or

$$d^2 = 180 \pm 72 = 252, \text{ or } 108.$$

$$\therefore \quad d = \sqrt{252}; \ \sqrt{108} = 15.9; \ 10.4 \text{ inches}$$

are the two diagonals of the given parallelogram.

Formula (iii) is a general formula for the diagonals of any parallelogram whose sides and angle are given.

Prob. 9. Find the area of the parallelogram of Prob. 8.

Solution. One of the properties of a parallelogram used in proving the result (L), article 5, is that a diagonal of the parallelogram divides it into two equal triangles. Therefore, the two triangles ABC and DCB in Fig. 88 are equal to one another, so that the area of the parallelogram is equal to twice the area of either triangle. According to formula (57), article 43, the area of $\triangle ABC$ is equal to $\tfrac{1}{2}bc \sin A$. The area of the parallelogram is, therefore,

$$K' = bc \sin A.$$

This is a general formula for the area of any parallelogram whose sides and angle are given, and states that *the area of a parallelogram equals the product of its sides by the sine of their included angle.*

Using the data of Prob. 8 in this area formula, the area of the given parallelogram is, therefore,

$$K' = 6 \times 12 \sin 60° = 72 \times .8660 = 62.4 \text{ sq. in.}$$

Prob. 10. Assuming the country between the towns of Prob. 7 to be flat and level, find the number of acres included between the straight roads joining them.

Solution. The straight roads joining the towns form the oblique triangle ABC of Fig. 87 with the sides $a = 14$, $b = 10$, $c = 15$ miles. By formulas (62), article 43, when

$$s = \tfrac{1}{2}(a + b + c), \quad K = \sqrt{s(s - a)(s - b)(s - c)}.$$

Using the given data, $s = \tfrac{1}{2}(14 + 10 + 15) = 19.5$; then,

$$s - a = 5.5, \quad s - b = 9.5, \quad s - c = 4.5 \text{ miles.}$$

Therefore

$$K = \sqrt{19.5 \times 5.5 \times 9.5 \times 4.5} = \sqrt{4585} = 67.7 \text{ sq. mi.}$$

To convert this into acres we have 1 sq. mi. = 640 acres.

$$\therefore \quad K = 67.7 \times 640 = 43{,}328 \text{ acres.}$$

In this article we have given the complete solutions of a number of problems involving simple applications of the sine law and one each illustrating simple applications of the cosine, segment and area laws. The tangent law, as noted before, is more convenient to use in cases where considerable precision is desired and the computations are carried out logarithmically. In the next article are given the solutions of several problems typical of those which arise in surveying, and requiring the application of various laws of the oblique triangle.

51. Problems in Surveying. In the following problems the statement will in each case be given in a general descriptive manner without data, so as to apply to any one of a certain class of problems. The data will then be given for an illustrative solution by specific reference to a sketch.

These problems serve two purposes: they illustrate the applications of trigonometry to practical measurements, and they show some of the methods and operations of the art and science of surveying.

In the computations, four-place tables will be used; in actual surveying, tables of six or seven places are used.

Prob. 1.   *To find the distance between two points not visible from each other.*

Fig. 89—*A* and *B* are the points.   Select a third point *C* from which *A* and *B* are visible and measure the distances *CA*, *CB* and the angle *ACB*.

If *CA* = 444.4 ft., *CB* = 222.8 ft., $\angle ACB$ = 17° 17.6′, find *AB*.

Solution.   Since two sides and the included angle are given, either the cosine or the tangent law applies, but since logarithms are to be used the tangent law is preferable.

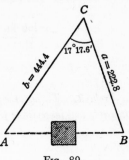

Fig. 89.

We shall use the tangent law to find $\angle B$ and then use the sine law to find *AB*.

The proper formulas are:

$$\tfrac{1}{2}(B + A) = 90° - \tfrac{1}{2}C, \quad \tan \tfrac{1}{2}(B - A) = \frac{(b - a)\tan \tfrac{1}{2}(B + A)}{b + a}.$$

$$\overline{AB} = \frac{b \sin C}{\sin B}.$$

Using the given data, and letting $\angle ACB = C$, $CA = b$, $CB = a$, we have

$$\tfrac{1}{2}(B + A) = 90° - \tfrac{1}{2}(17° 17.6′) = 90° - 8° 38.8′ = 81° 21.2′.$$

$$b - a = 444.4 - 222.8 = 221.6, \quad b + a = 444.4 + 222.8 = 667.2,$$

$$\therefore \quad \tan \tfrac{1}{2}(B - A) = \frac{221.6 \tan 81° 21.2′}{667.2}.$$

$$
\begin{aligned}
\log 221.6 &= 2.3456 \\
+\log \tan 81° 21.2′ &= 10.8180 - 10 \\
\hline
\log \text{Prod.} &= 13.1636 - 10 \\
-\log 667.2 &= 2.8243 \\
\hline
\log \tan \tfrac{1}{2}(B - A) &= 10.3393 - 10 \\
\tfrac{1}{2}(B - A) &= 65° 24′ \\
+\tfrac{1}{2}(B + A) &= 81° 21.2′ \\
\hline
B &= 146° 45.2′
\end{aligned}
$$

$$\therefore \quad \overline{AB} = \frac{444.4 \sin 17° 17.6′}{\sin 146° 45.2′}$$

$$\log 444.4 = 2.6478$$
$$+\log \sin 17° 17.6' = 9.4731 - 10$$

$$\log \text{Prod.} = 12.1209 - 10$$
$$-\log \sin 146° 45.2' = 9.7390 - 10$$

$$\log AB = 2.3819$$

$$\overline{AB} = 240.9 \text{ ft.}$$

Prob. 2. *To find the distance from one point to a second point which is invisible and inaccessible from the first.*

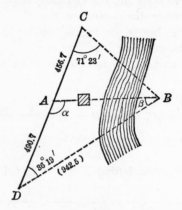

FIG. 90.

Fig. 90—*A* and *B* are the two points. Select two other points *C*, *D* so that *C*, *D*, *A* are in the same straight line and both *A* and *B* are visible from *C* and from *D*. Measure *AC*, *AD*, ∠*ACB* (= *C*), and ∠*ABD* (= *D*).

If

$$AC = 456.7 \text{ ft.,} \qquad AD = 490.7 \text{ ft.,}$$

$$C = 71° 23', \qquad D = 36° 19', \qquad \text{find } AB.$$

Solution. Let ∠*CBD* = *B*; then *B* = 180° − (*C* + *D*) = 180° − 107° 42′ = 72° 18′, *CD* = *AC* + *AD* = 9474. ft., and in oblique △*BCD*, $\overline{BD} = \dfrac{\overline{CD} \sin C}{\sin B}.$

$$\log 947.4 = \quad 2.9765$$
$$+\log \sin 71° \, 23' = \quad 9.9767 - 10$$
$$\overline{}$$
$$\log \text{Prod.} = \quad 12.9532 - 10$$
$$-\log \sin 72° \, 18' = \quad 9.9789 - 10$$
$$\overline{}$$
$$\log BD = \quad 2.9743$$

$$\therefore \quad \overline{BD} = 942.5 \text{ ft.}$$

With BD now known, we have in oblique $\triangle ADB$ the two sides AD, BD and included $\angle D$. As in Prob. 1 above we use the tangent and sine laws. If we put $\angle DAB = \alpha$, $\angle DBA = \beta$, the formulas are:

$$\tfrac{1}{2}(\alpha + \beta) = 90° - \tfrac{1}{2}D, \quad \tan \tfrac{1}{2}(\alpha - \beta) = \frac{(\overline{BD} - \overline{AD}) \tan \tfrac{1}{2}(\alpha + \beta)}{\overline{BD} + \overline{AD}},$$

$$\overline{AB} = \frac{\overline{BD} \sin D}{\sin \alpha}.$$

Using the given data and the value of BD as found, we have

$$\tfrac{1}{2}(\alpha + \beta) = 90° - \tfrac{1}{2}(36° \, 19') = 71° \, 50.5', \quad BD - \overline{AD} = 451.8 \text{ ft.,}$$

$BD + \overline{AD} = 1433.2$ ft., and therefore,

$$\tan \tfrac{1}{2}(\alpha - \beta) = \frac{451.8 \tan 71° \, 50.5'}{1433.2}.$$

$$\log 451.8 = \quad 2.6549$$
$$+\log \tan 71° \, 50.5' = \quad 10.4842 - 10$$
$$\overline{}$$
$$\log \text{Prod.} = \quad 13.1391 - 10$$
$$-\log 1433.2 = \quad 3.1563$$
$$\overline{}$$
$$\log \tan \tfrac{1}{2}(\alpha - \beta) = \quad 9.9828 - 10$$

$$\tfrac{1}{2}(\alpha - \beta) = \quad 43° \, 52'$$
$$+\tfrac{1}{2}(\alpha + \beta) = \quad 71° \, 50.5'$$
$$\overline{}$$
$$\alpha = \quad 115° \, 42.5'$$

$$\therefore \quad \overline{AB} = \frac{942.5 \sin 36° \, 19'}{\sin 115° \, 42.5'}.$$

$$\log 942.5 = 2.9743$$
$$+\log \sin 36° 19' = 9.7725 - 10$$

$$\log \text{Prod.} = 12.7468 - 10$$
$$-\log \sin 115° 42.5' = 9.9547 - 10$$

$$\log \overline{AB} = 2.7921$$

$$\therefore \quad \overline{AB} = 619.6 \text{ ft.}$$

Prob. 3.   To find the distance between two inaccessible points.

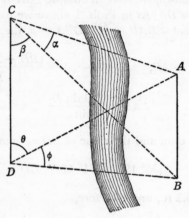

FIG. 91.

Fig. 91—*A, B* are the points.   Select two other points *C, D* from
each of which both *A* and *B* are visible.   Measure the distance *CD*
and the angles $ACB = \alpha$, $BCD = \beta$, $ADC = \theta$, $ADB = \phi$.

If

$$CD = 456.3 \text{ ft.,} \qquad \alpha = 30° 41', \qquad \beta = 40° 15',$$
$$\theta = 35° 16', \qquad \phi = 56° 47', \qquad \text{find } AB.$$

Solution.   The procedure in this case is to find either the distances
CA and *CB* and then with these two sides and the included angle
known, to find the third side *AB* of the triangle *ABC;* or in the same
way to find *DA* and *DB* and then find *AB* in $\triangle ABD$.   We shall
use $\triangle ABD$.

In order to find the distances *DA* and *DB* we use the triangles *DCA*
and *DCB*, respectively, and apply the sine law to each.   Since the
number of steps in the complete calculation is large we shall use the

direct method and the slide rule rather than logarithms. This will illustrate the method and allow attention to be concentrated on the procedure, even though it may not be as precise as the logarithmic method.

Let $\angle CAD = A$ and $\angle CBD = B$. Then in $\triangle DCA$, $A = 180° - \angle ACD + \angle ADC) = 180° - (\alpha + \beta + \theta)$; hence, $A = 180° - 106° 2' = 73° 48'$. Also in the same triangle,

$$\overline{DA}/\sin \angle ACD = \overline{CD}/\sin A,$$

or

$$\overline{DA} = \frac{\overline{CD} \sin \angle ACD}{\sin A}.$$

From the data, $CD = 456.3$, $\angle ACD = \alpha + \beta = 70° 56'$, $A = 73° 48'$.

$$\therefore \quad \overline{DA} = \frac{456.3 \sin 70° 56'}{\sin 73° 48'} = \frac{456.3 \times .9451}{.9603} = 449 \text{ ft.}$$

Similarly, $\angle B = 180° - (\angle BCD + \angle BDC) = 180° - (\beta + \theta + \phi)$; hence,

$B = 180° - 132° 18' = 47° 42'$. And in $\triangle DCB$, $\overline{DB}/\sin \beta = \overline{CD}/\sin B.$

$$\therefore \quad \overline{DB} = \frac{\overline{CD} \sin \beta}{\sin B}.$$

From the data as before,

$$CD = 456.3, \quad \beta = 40° 15', \quad B = 47° 42'.$$

$$\therefore \quad \overline{DB} = \frac{456.3 \sin 40° 15'}{\sin 47° 42'} = \frac{456.3 \times .6461}{.7396} = 399 \text{ ft.}$$

Having found DA and DB, then in the triangle ADB by the cosine law we have,

$$\overline{AB}^2 = \overline{DA}^2 + \overline{DB}^2 - 2\overline{DA} \cdot \overline{DB} \cos \phi,$$

with

$$DA = 449, \quad DB = 399, \quad \phi = 56° 47'.$$

$$\therefore \quad \overline{AB}^2 = (449)^2 + (399)^2 - 2 \times 449 \times 399 \cos 56° 47'$$

$$= 201{,}600 + 159{,}200 - 358{,}300 \times .5478,$$

$$= 360{,}800 - 196{,}100 = 164{,}700.$$

$$\therefore \quad \overline{AB} = \sqrt{164700} = 406 \text{ ft.}$$

Prob. 4. *To find the distance between two inaccessible points when both are visible from only one accessible point.*

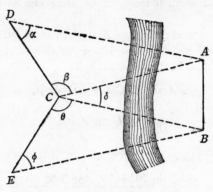

Fig. 92.

Fig. 92—*A, B* are the two points and *C* the one from which both are visible. Select a point *D* from which *A* and *C* are visible, and another point *E* from which *B* and *C* are visible. Measure *CD* and *CE*, and measure the following angles:

$$\angle CDA = \alpha, \quad \angle DCA = \beta, \quad \angle ACB = \delta, \quad \angle ECB = \theta, \quad \angle CEB = \phi.$$

If

$$CD = 943.4 \text{ ft.,} \quad CE = 673.3 \text{ ft.,} \quad \alpha = 72° 9', \quad \beta = 60° 17'$$

$$\delta = 32° 15', \quad \theta = 67° 34', \quad \phi = 19° 15', \quad \text{find } AB.$$

Solution. The procedure in this case is to solve $\triangle CAD$ for CA and $\triangle CBE$ for CB, and with CA and CB thus known to solve $\triangle ACB$ for AB.

Let $\angle CAD = A'$, $\angle CBE = B'$. Then,

$$A' = 180° - (\alpha + \beta) = 180° - 132° 27' = 47° 33',$$

$$B' = 180° - (\theta + \phi) = 180° - 86° 49' = 93° 11'.$$

In oblique $\triangle CAD$, $\overline{CA}/\sin \alpha = \overline{CD}/\sin A'$, $\therefore CA = \dfrac{\overline{CD} \sin \alpha}{\sin A'}.$

In oblique $\triangle CBE$, $\overline{CB}/\sin \phi = \overline{CE}/\sin B'$, $\therefore \overline{CB} = \dfrac{\overline{CE} \sin \phi}{\sin B'}.$

$$\therefore \quad \overline{CA} = \frac{943.4 \sin 72° 9'}{\sin 47° 33'}. \qquad \therefore \quad \overline{CB} = \frac{673.3 \sin 19° 15'}{\sin 93° 11'}.$$

$$\begin{array}{ll}
\log 943.4 = \quad 2.9747 & \log 673.3 = \quad 2.8282 \\
+\log \sin 72°\ 9' = \quad 9.9786 - 10 & +\log \sin 19°\ 15' = \quad 9.5181 - 10 \\
\hline
\log \text{Prod.} = 12.9533 - 10 & \log \text{Prod.} = 12.3463 - 10 \\
-\log \sin 47°\ 33' = \quad 9.8680 - 10 & -\log \sin 93°\ 11' = \quad 9.9993 - 10 \\
\hline
\log \overline{CA} = \quad 3.0853 & \log \overline{CB} = \quad 2.3470 \\
CA = 1217 \text{ ft.} & CB = 222.3 \text{ ft.}
\end{array}$$

With CA and CB and their included angle δ now known the triangle ABC is solved for AB by applying the tangent and sine laws. If we let $\angle CAB = A$ and $\angle CBA = B$ the formulas are:

$$\tfrac{1}{2}(B + A) = 90° - \tfrac{1}{2}\delta, \quad \tan \tfrac{1}{2}(B - A) = \frac{(\overline{CA} - \overline{CB}) \tan \tfrac{1}{2}(B + A)}{\overline{CA} + \overline{CB}},$$

$$\overline{AB} = \frac{\overline{CA} \sin \delta}{\sin B}.$$

Using the values $\delta = 32°\ 15'$, $CA = 1217$ ft., $CB = 222.3$ ft., then

$$\tfrac{1}{2}(B + A) = 73°\ 52.5', \quad CA - CB = 994.7, \quad CA + CB = 1439.3 \text{ ft.}$$

$$\therefore \quad \tan \tfrac{1}{2}(B - A) = \frac{994.7 \tan 73°\ 52.5'}{1439.3},$$

$$\overline{AB} = \frac{1217 \sin 32°\ 15'}{\sin B}.$$

$$\begin{array}{l}
\log 994.7 = \quad 2.9977 \\
+\log \tan 73°\ 52.5' = 10.5389 - 10 \\
\hline
\log \text{Prod.} = 13.5366 - 10 \\
-\log 1439.3 = \quad 3.1582 \\
\hline
\log \tan \tfrac{1}{2}(B - A) = 10.3784 - 10 \\
\tfrac{1}{2}(B - A) = \quad 67°\ 18' \\
+\tfrac{1}{2}(B + A) = \quad 73°\ 52.5' \\
\hline
B = 141°\ 10.5' \\
\log 1217 = \quad 3.0853 \\
+\log \sin 32°\ 15' = \quad 9.7272 - 10 \\
\hline
\log \text{Prod.} = 12.8125 - 10 \\
-\log \sin 141°\ 10.5' = \quad 9.7973 - 10 \\
\hline
\log \overline{AB} = \quad 3.0152 \\
AB = 1036 \text{ ft.}
\end{array}$$

Prob. 5. *To run a straight line through an obstacle.*

Fig. 93—*AB* is the line and *F* is the obstacle. The line is run up to the obstacle, the portion *AC* being laid off. From the point *C* on

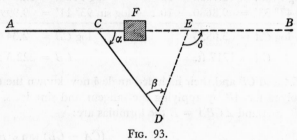

Fig. 93.

the line, a line *CD* is laid off making the angle *BCD* = α, and at *D* the angle *CDE* = β is laid off. The line *DE* is then laid off in the direction given by this angle and must be of such length as to meet the required line at *E*. At the point *E* on the original line the angle *DEB* = δ must then be laid off so that *EB* is the continuation of *AC*.

If *CD* = 144.3 ft., α = 19° 53′, β = 140° 10′, find δ, *DE* and *CE*.

Solution. By the principle (*K*), article 5, exterior ∠δ of △*CDE* equals the sum of the opposite interior angles α and β.

$$\therefore \quad \delta = \alpha + \beta = 160° 3'.$$

Since the two angles α, β and the included side *CD* of △*CDE* are known, it is solved by the sine law for *DE* and *CE*. We have ∠*E* = ∠*DEC* = 180° − δ = 19° 57′. Then by the sine law

$$\overline{DE} = \frac{\overline{CD} \sin \alpha}{\sin E}, \quad \overline{CE} = \frac{\overline{CD} \sin \beta}{\sin E}.$$

Using the values *CD* = 144.3, α = 19° 53′, β = 140° 10′, *E* = 19°, 57′, these formulas give

$$\overline{DE} = \frac{144.3 \sin 19° 53'}{\sin 19° 57'}.$$

$$
\begin{array}{rl}
\log 144.3 = & 2.1593 \\
+\log \sin 19° 53' = & 9.5316 - 10 \\
\hline
\log \text{Prod.} = & 11.6909 - 10 \\
-\log \sin 19° 57' = & 9.5330 - 10 \\
\hline
\log DE = & 2.1579 \\
\end{array}
$$

$$DE = 143.8 \text{ ft.}$$

$$\overline{CE} = \frac{144.3 \sin 140° 10'}{\sin 19° 57'}.$$

$$\log 144.3 = 2.1593$$
$$+\log \sin 140° 10' = 9.8066 - 10$$

$$\log \text{Prod.} = 11.9659 - 10$$
$$- \log \sin 19° 57' = 9.5330 - 10$$

$$\log CE = 2.4329$$
$$CE = 271.0 \text{ ft.}$$

52. Parallax of a Heavenly Body. The *equatorial parallax* of a heavenly body with reference to the earth was defined in article 31 as the angle APB in Fig. 60. This angle is found from measurements made simultaneously at two points on the earth's surface at a known distance apart. The measurements and calculations necessary to determine the parallax will be described in connection with Fig. 94.

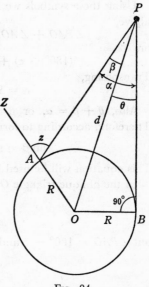

Fig. 94.

In Fig. 94, P represents the position of the heavenly body and the circle with center at O represents the earth. A and B are the two observation points and the arc distance $\overarc{AB}$ between them is known. The body at P is observed from B in the direction BP at the moment when it is on the horizon, so that the angle OBP is 90°. At the same moment (by previous agreement) P is observed from A in the direction AP. The telescope at A is then turned to the direction AZ, Z being the point in the sky directly overhead at A and called the *zenith*, and AZ, therefore, in line with the radius OA. From these two readings the angle ZAP is known. This angle is called the *apparent zenith distance* of P as seen at A. The angle OAP is then known also, since it is the supplement of the apparent zenith distance.

The angle AOB at the center of the earth is also known. For the arc distance $\overarc{AB}$ is known and $\angle AOB$ is the same part of 360° as $\overarc{AB}$ is of the earth's circumference. Therefore, in the quadrilateral $AOBPA$ the angles PAO, AOB, OBP are known, and since a quadrilateral can be divided into two triangles each of whose angles totals 180°, the sum of the interior angles of the quadrilateral $AOBPA$ is 360°, and, therefore, $\angle APB$ is known.

Draw the line OP from the center of the earth to the heavenly body. The angle OPB is the *equatorial parallax* of the body at P and it is this angle which we wish to find.

In Fig. 94, let R represent the earth's radius OA, OB and let the distance $OP = d$. Also, let $\angle OPA = \beta$, $\angle OPB = \theta$, $\angle BPA = \alpha$, $\angle ZAP = z$. Then, $\angle AOB$ is known, $\angle OBP = 90°$, $\angle z$ is measured, and $\angle PAO = 180° - z$.

Using these symbols we have in the quadrilateral $AOBPA$, as seen above,

$$\angle PAO + \angle AOB + \angle OBP + \angle BPA = 360°,$$

or,

$$(180° - z) + \angle AOB + 90° + \alpha = 360°.$$

Transposing,

$$\alpha = 90° - (\angle AOB - z). \tag{63}$$

Also, $\theta + \beta = \alpha$, or $\beta = \alpha - \theta$, and hence, $\sin \beta = \sin (a - \theta)$. Therefore, according to formula (100), article 58,

$$\sin \beta = \sin \alpha \cos \theta - \cos \alpha \sin \theta. \tag{64}$$

This equation will be used below.

In the oblique triangle OPA, by the sine law,

$$\frac{\sin \beta}{\sin \angle PAO} = \frac{R}{d};$$

but $\angle PAO = 180° - z$ and, therefore, $\sin \angle PAO = \sin z$. Hence,

$$\frac{\sin \beta}{\sin z} = \frac{R}{d}.$$

Also, in the right triangle OBP, $\dfrac{R}{d} = \sin \theta$. Therefore,

$$\frac{\sin \beta}{\sin z} = \sin \theta,$$

$$\therefore \quad \sin \beta = \sin z \sin \theta. \tag{65}$$

Comparing equations (65) and (64) we have at once

$$\sin z \sin \theta = \sin \alpha \cos \theta - \cos \alpha \sin \theta. \tag{66}$$

In this equation z is known from measurement and α is given by equation (63). The angle θ is, therefore, the only unknown in (66) and the equation can, therefore, be solved for θ.

Transposing equation (66),

$$\sin z \sin \theta + \cos \alpha \sin \theta = \sin \alpha \cos \theta.$$

Factoring,

$$(\sin z + \cos \alpha) \sin \theta = \sin \alpha \cos \theta.$$

Dividing this by $\cos \theta$ and by $(\sin z + \cos \alpha)$ we get

$$\frac{\sin \theta}{\cos \theta} = \frac{\sin \alpha}{\sin z + \cos \alpha}.$$

But $\sin \theta / \cos \theta = \tan \theta$. We have therefore, finally,

$$\tan \theta = \frac{\sin \alpha}{\sin z + \cos \alpha}. \tag{67}$$

This is our *solution formula* for the equatorial parallax θ. When the distance AB is known and the apparent zenith distance is measured, then z is known and by (63) α is known. These values of z and α in the solution formula (67) give $\tan \theta$ and the parallax θ is then read from the tables.

Problem. If in a certain case the distance on the earth between two observation stations is 8280 miles and the apparent zenith distance of the sun is $30° \, 13.2''$ at one station when it is just setting at the other, find the equatorial parallax of the sun.

Solution. Using the value of the earth's diameter found in Prob. 1, article 31, the circumference is $\pi d = 7920\pi = 24{,}840$ miles. Then in Fig. 94, $\overparen{AB}$: (circumf.)::8280 : 24840 and from this proportion $\overparen{AB} = \frac{1}{3}$ (circumf.). Therefore, $\angle AOB = \frac{1}{3}(360°) = 120°$. Also, the apparent zenith distance is $z = 30° \, 13.2''$.

Using these values of $\angle AOB$ and z in formula (63) we have,

$$\alpha = 90° - (120° - 30° \, 13.2'') = 13.2''.$$

These values substituted in the solution formula (67) give, when seven-place tables are used,

$$\tan \theta = \frac{\sin 13.2''}{\sin 30° \, 13.2'' + \cos 13.2''} = \frac{\sin 13.2''}{.5000554 + 1.0000000}.$$

$$\therefore \quad \tan \theta = \frac{\sin 13.2''}{1.5000554}.$$

This computation is best carried out logarithmically.   Using the seven-place tables we have:

$$\log \sin 13.2'' = 5.8059551 - 10$$
$$-\log 1.5000554 = 0.1761075$$

$$\log \tan \theta = 5.6297476 - 10$$
$$\theta = 8.8''.$$

This is the value which was used in article 31.

The accurate measurement of the angles involved in determining parallax is a matter of some difficulty, requiring great precaution and many corrections and compensations for error.

53. Annual Parallax and Star Distances.   In article 31 the *annual parallax* of a heavenly body is defined and in Fig. 59 of that article it is represented by the angle *APB*. In Prob. 4 of the same article the distance of a star is calculated on the basis of $\triangle APB$, Fig. 59, or $\triangle E'PE$, Fig. 63, being an isosceles triangle, so that in Fig. 63, $\angle PSE$ is a right angle and $PE' = PE$.

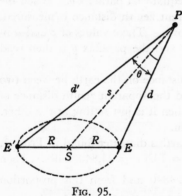

Fig. 95.

This is not always the case, however, and therefore the star's distance cannot always be determined by means of a right triangle. It is generally necessary to make use of an oblique triangle. In order to explain this method, Fig. 59 is here reproduced with the lettering of Fig. 63 (Fig. 95).

Here the dotted circle with center at S is the annual path of the earth about the sun (S) and E, E' represent two positions of the earth six months apart in its orbit. The line EE' is thus a straight line passing through the sun and since, as found in Prob. 2, article 31, $ES = E'S = 92,919,800$ miles, $EE' = 185,839,600$ or about $185,840,000$ miles. We may call this distance the *diameter* of the earth's orbit. Let it be represented by D.

If, then, P represents the position of a fixed star in the heavens, EP is the earth-star distance at a certain time, and $E'P$ is that distance six months later (or earlier). Then $\triangle EPE'$ is an oblique triangle and $\angle EPE'$ is the angle of *annual parallax* of the star. Let θ represent this angle, and let $EP = d$, $E'P = d'$. Then, since EE' is known, it is only necessary to measure the angles PEE' and $PE'E$, or SEP and $SE'P$, in order to find θ, d, d'.

The angle SEP is measured by sighting the telescope on the sun (S) and then on the star (P). The angle, through which it is turned, is $\angle SEP$; call this $\angle E$. Similarly $\angle SE'P = E'$ is measured six months later.

Problem.   At a certain time the sun-earth-star angle of a certain star is $95°\ 27'\ 45''$ and six months later it is $84°\ 32'\ 13.6''$. Find the annual parallax of the star, its distance from the earth in the first position, and its distance from the sun.

Solution.   Let E (Fig. 95) be the first position of the earth and E' the second. Then $\angle E = 95°\ 27'\ 45''$, $\angle E' = 84°\ 32'\ 13.6''$ and in $\triangle EPE'$, $\theta = 180° - (E + E')$. Hence,

$$\theta = 1.4'',$$

is the annual parallax of the star.

To find the distance $EP = d$ from the earth in its first position we have in oblique $\triangle EPE'$, $d/\sin E' = D/\sin \theta$ and

$$d = \frac{D \sin E'}{\sin \theta}.$$

The data are:

$$D = 185{,}840{,}000 \text{ mi.}, \quad E' = 84°\ 32'\ 13.6'', \quad \theta = 1.4''.$$

$$\therefore \quad d = \frac{185{,}840{,}000 \sin 84°\ 32'\ 13.6''}{\sin 1.4''}.$$

Using seven-place logarithms the computation is as follows:

$$
\begin{aligned}
\log 185{,}840{,}000 &= 8.2691392 \\
+\log \sin 84°\ 32'\ 13.6'' &= 9.9980229 - 10 \\
\hline
\log \text{Prod.} &= 18.2671621 - 10 \\
-\log \sin 1.4'' &= 4.8059869 - 10 \\
\hline
\log d &= 13.4611752 \\
d &= 28{,}918{,}460{,}000{,}000 \text{ miles.}
\end{aligned}
$$

Expressed in light years, this gives for the earth-star distance,

$$d = \frac{28{,}918{,}460{,}000{,}000}{5{,}880{,}003{,}000{,}000} = 4.918 \text{ light yrs.}$$

The distance from the sun to the star is the distance SP in Fig. 95. In order to find this distance, oblique $\triangle SEP$ is to be solved for SP with ES, EP and $\angle SEP$ known. This triangle is shown separately in Fig. 96, the angles ESP, EPS being indicated by α, β, respectively, and

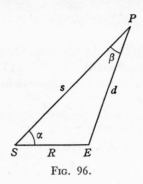

Fig. 96.

the distances ES, SP, by R, s, respectively. From the original data and the result of the solution for d the data for this triangle are:

$R = 92,919,800$ mi., $\quad d = 28,918,460,000,000$ mi., $\quad E = 95° 27' 45''$.

In order to solve $\triangle SEP$ for s, with R, d/E, known, we use the tangent and sine laws, the formulas being:

$$\tfrac{1}{2}(\alpha + \beta) = 90° - \tfrac{1}{2}E, \quad \tan \tfrac{1}{2}(\alpha - \beta) = \frac{(d - R) \tan \tfrac{1}{2}(\alpha + \beta)}{d + R},$$

$$s = \frac{d \sin E}{\sin \alpha}.$$

The data when substituted in these formulas give,

$$\tfrac{1}{2}(\alpha + \beta) = 42° 16' 7.5'', \quad d - R = 28,918,367,080,200 \text{ mi.,}$$
$$d + R = 28,918,552,919,800 \text{ mi.}$$

$$\therefore \quad \tan \tfrac{1}{2}(\alpha - \beta) = \frac{28,918,367,080,200 \tan 42° 16' 7.5''}{28,918,552,919,800},$$

or, very nearly

$$\tan \tfrac{1}{2}(\alpha - \beta) = \frac{28,918,367 \tan 42° 16' 7.5''}{28,918,553},$$

and

$$s = \frac{28,918,460,000,000 \sin 95° 27' 45''}{\sin \alpha}.$$

The indicated computations are here carried out with seven-place logarithms.

$$\log 28918367 = 7.4611737$$
$$+\log \tan 42° 16' 7.5'' = 9.9585321 - 10$$
$$\overline{\log \text{Prod.} = 17.4197058 - 10}$$
$$-\log 28918553 = 7.4611766$$
$$\overline{\log \tan \tfrac{1}{2}(\alpha - \beta) = 9.9585292 - 10}$$

$$\tfrac{1}{2}(\alpha - \beta) = 42° 16' \ 6.8''$$
$$+\tfrac{1}{2}(\alpha + \beta) = 42° 16' \ 7.5''$$
$$\overline{\alpha = 84° 32' 14.3''}$$

$$\log 28918460000000 = 13.4611752$$
$$+\log \sin 95° 27' 45'' = 9.9980233 - 10$$
$$\overline{\log \text{Prod.} = 23.4591985 - 10}$$
$$-\log \sin 84° 32' 14.3'' = 9.9980231 - 10$$
$$\overline{\log s = 13.4611754}$$

$$s = 28,918,470,000,000 \text{ miles.}$$

The difference between the sun-star and earth-star distances is, therefore,

$$s - d = 10,000,000 \text{ miles,}$$

but, while 10 millions of miles is a distance inconceivably great, it is only one part in 2891847, that is, one part in nearly three million, when compared with the total. The difference is, therefore, extremely small.

In order to determine these distances with greater precision, the angles are measured with extreme care and usually to the hundredth of a second, or by repetition and averaging, to the thousandth of a second, and 10-place tables are used in the computations. The computations given in this article are to be taken simply as illustrations of the methods, which are in themselves of great interest, beauty and, in principle, simplicity.

54. Problems for Solution.

1. At a distance of 40 feet from the foot of a tree on a slope, the angle of elevation of the top of the tree *above the slope* is 41° 19′, and 60 feet farther down the slope it is 23° 45′. How high is the tree?

2. A vertical tower makes an angle of 113° 12′ with a slope on which it stands, and at a distance of 89 feet down the slope the elevation of the top above the slope is 23° 27′. Find its height.

3. In order to find the distance between two objects (A, B) a third point (C) was chosen and the distances CA, CB and the angle ACB were measured. If $CA = 426$ ft., $CB = 322$ ft., $\angle ACB = 68°\ 42′$, find the distance AB.

4. The diagonals of a parallelogram are 5 and 6 inches and meet at an angle of 49° 18′. Find the sides. (Note: The diagonals bisect each other.)

5. Two meteorological observers 700 feet apart and on opposite sides of a cloud find its angles of elevation to be 44° 56′ and 36° 4′. How high is the cloud?

6. Half an hour after the observations of Prob. 5 the observers in the same positions find the angles of elevation of the same cloud to be, respectively, 26° 20′ and 70° 35′. If it moves horizontally and uniformly, how fast is it moving?

7. Two inaccessible objects (A, B) are each viewed from two stations (C, D) 562 yards apart and on the same side of the line joining the two objects. The following angles are measured: $\angle ACB = 62°\ 12′$, $\angle BCD = 41°\ 8′$, $\angle ADB = 60°\ 49′$, $\angle ADC = 34°\ 51′$. Find the distance (AB) between the two objects.

8. The distances between three cities (A, B, C) at the vertices of a triangle are 165, 72, 185 miles. The second is due east from the first and the third is north of the line joining the first two. In what direction is it from the first?

9. A ladder 52 feet long is set 20 feet in front of an inclined embankment and reaches 40 feet up its face. Find the inclination of the face of the embankment to the horizontal.

10. If the ladder in Prob. 9 is to be set so that it makes an angle of 45 degrees with the horizontal, how far must it be placed from the foot of the embankment and how far up the face will it reach?

11. Under what visual angle does an observer view a painting which is seven feet high if he stands so that his eye is five feet from the bottom and eight feet from the top of the painting?

12. The sides of a triangle are 14.6, 16.7, 18.8 inches. Find the altitude drawn on the longest side as base.

13. From a 140-foot cliff on one bank of a river, a surveyor reads the angles of depression of the top and bottom of the cliff-bank on the opposite side. The angles are 40 and 80 degrees and the width of the river is not known. Find the height of the cliff.

14. A triangular plate of metal one inch thick measures 10, 12, 16 inches on the edges and weighs 18 pounds. What is the weight per cubic inch?

15. The sides of a triangle are 17, 21, 28 inches. Find the length of the line from the middle of the longest side to the vertex of the opposite angle.

16. An irregularly shaped courtyard is bounded by four walls of 10, 12, 14, 16 feet length and the angle between the first two is 70 degrees. If the cost of paving is 50c per square yard, find the cost of paving the courtyard.

17. A straight road crosses a straight stream at an angle of 72 degrees. A

straight fence crosses the stream 100 yards from the road crossing and meets the road 150 yards from the crossing. How long is the fence and how much land is enclosed by the fence, road and stream?

18. When the moon is just setting at a certain place on the earth its apparent zenith distance at a place 7452 miles away is $19° 5\frac{1}{2}'$. Find the moon's equatorial parallax.

19. Two sides of a triangular field are 180 and 210 feet and the angle between these two sides is 120°. Find the area of the field and the length of the third side.

20. Town Y lies 25 miles west of town X, and town Z is farther south than either X or Y. The distance from X to Z is 17 miles, and from Y to Z is 19 miles. In what direction is Z from X?

21. Two cyclists pedal away from the same place at the same time. One goes south at the rate of 13 miles per hour, and the other goes in a direction 46° 57′ east of south at 11 miles per hour. How far apart are they at the end of three hours after the start?

22. At the foot of a street hangs an arc light which is 19 ft. 6 in. above the ground. The street slopes upward from this point at an incline of 6° 57′ above the horizontal. How far up the slope is the point at which the rays from the arc light meet the street surface at an angle of 12° 13′?

23. Two villages are 5.0843 miles and 7.469 miles from a pumping station, and the angle subtended by the villages at the station is 59° 42′. The shortest pipe line possible is to be built from the station to the straight road joining the villages. Find the length of the line.

24. Upon the top of a store building 125 feet high stands an electric sign which at a horizontal distance of 200 feet from the foot of the building subtends an angle of 3° in a vertical plane. What is the height of the sign?

25. A corner lot of land fronts 100 feet on one street and 80 feet on the other street, the corner angle between the streets being 82° 25′. The other two sides of the lot are perpendicular to the lines of the streets. What is the lot worth at 25 cents per square foot?

Chapter 10

RELATIONS AMONG
THE TRIGONOMETRIC FUNCTIONS

55. Introduction. In the preceding chapters we have had frequent occasion to make use of the relations among the functions of an angle which were developed in article 8. Also, in article 41 we have made use of a formula giving the value of the expression $\dfrac{\sin A + \sin B}{\sin A - \sin B}$ in terms of functions of the sum and difference of the angles, $(A + B)$ and $(A - B)$, and in article 52 we used the formula giving the sine of the difference of two angles, $\sin (\alpha - \theta)$, in terms of the functions of the separate angles, $\sin \alpha$, $\cos \theta$, etc.

In certain parts of trigonometry, the so-called algebraic or *analytical trigonometry*, and in the higher mathematics, such as the *calculus*, such formulas and many other similar relations are very much used. They are also very useful in the computation of the trigonometric tables. In addition to their wide usefulness, they are of the greatest interest and beauty in themselves.

For these reasons we give in this chapter a brief introduction to analytical trigonometry, by developing a few of the *relations among the trigonometric functions* of an angle and of more than one angle.

56. Relations among Functions of One Angle. For use in what follows, we recall here some of the relations given in article 8. Letting x represent any angle, expressed in either degree measure or radian measure, formula (11) of article 8 can be written

$$\frac{\sin x}{\cos x} = \tan x. \tag{68}$$

Similarly, formulas (12), (13) become

$$\tan x = \frac{1}{\cot x}, \quad \cot x = \frac{1}{\tan x}, \tag{69}$$

$$\cot x = \frac{\cos x}{\sin x} \tag{70}$$

and by (14),

$$\left.\begin{array}{ll} \sec x = \dfrac{1}{\cos x}, & \csc x = \dfrac{1}{\sin x}, \\[2mm] \cos x = \dfrac{1}{\sec x}, & \sin x = \dfrac{1}{\csc x}. \end{array}\right\} \tag{71}$$

From formulas (69), (71), we have at once by simple algebraic transformation,

$$\left.\begin{array}{l} \sin x \cdot \csc x = 1 \\ \cos x \cdot \sec x = 1 \\ \tan x \cdot \cot x = 1. \end{array}\right\} \tag{72}$$

Also, formula (16) for the angle x is

$$\sin^2 x + \cos^2 x = 1. \tag{73}$$

If we divide this equation by $\cos^2 x$, we get $\dfrac{\sin^2 x}{\cos^2 x} + 1 = \dfrac{1}{\cos^2 x}$, and this can be written

$$\left(\frac{\sin x}{\cos x}\right)^2 + 1 = \left(\frac{1}{\cos x}\right)^2.$$

Making use of (11) and (71), therefore, we have finally,

$$\tan^2 x + 1 = \sec^2 x.$$

$$\therefore \quad \sec^2 x - \tan^2 x = 1. \tag{74}$$

If (73) is divided by $\sin^2 x$ we get, similarly, $1 + \left(\dfrac{\cos x}{\sin x}\right)^2 = \left(\dfrac{1}{\sin x}\right)^2$, and hence, $1 + \cot^2 x = \csc^2 x$, or

$$\csc^2 x - \cot^2 x = 1. \tag{75}$$

By means of the formulas given above any one of the functions of an angle can be expressed in terms of any other, and all may be expressed in terms of any one. Thus, for example, to express all the functions in terms of the sine, we have from (73)

$$\cos^2 x = 1 - \sin^2 x,$$

$$\therefore \quad \cos x = \sqrt{1 - \sin^2 x}. \tag{76}$$

Then, since by (68) $\tan x = \sin x / \cos x$, we have,

$$\tan x = \frac{\sin x}{\sqrt{1 - \sin^2 x}}, \tag{77}$$

and since $\cot x = 1/\tan x$ this gives

$$\cot x = \frac{\sqrt{1 - \sin^2 x}}{\sin x}. \tag{78}$$

Similarly, $\sec x = 1/\cos x$ and using (76) this gives

$$\sec x = \frac{1}{\sqrt{1 - \sin^2 x}}, \tag{79}$$

and we already have

$$\csc x = \frac{1}{\sin x}. \tag{80}$$

Formulas (76)–(80) give all the other functions in terms of the sine. Similarly, all may be expressed in terms of $\cos x$, $\tan x$, etc. These transformations are left as exercises for the reader.

To express any one function, the sine, say, in terms of each of the others, each of the equations (76)–(80) may be solved algebraically for $\sin x$ or we may proceed independently as was done in deriving (76)–(80). Thus from (73) we have $\sin^2 x = 1 - \cos^2 x$ and therefore,

$$\sin x = \sqrt{1 - \cos^2 x}. \tag{81}$$

From (68) $\sin x = \tan x \cdot \cos x = \tan x \cdot \dfrac{1}{\sec x}$. But, from (74) $\sec x = \sqrt{1 + \tan^2 x}$; therefore,

$$\sin x = \frac{\tan x}{\sqrt{1 + \tan^2 x}}. \tag{82}$$

Also, $\sin x = 1/\csc x$, and from (75) $\csc x = \sqrt{1 + \cot^2 x}$; hence

$$\sin x = \frac{1}{\sqrt{1 + \cot^2 x}}. \tag{83}$$

If in (73) we put $\cos x = 1/\sec x$ and transpose we get,

$$\sin^2 x = 1 - \frac{1}{\sec^2 x} = \frac{\sec^2 x - 1}{\sec^2 x}.$$

$$\therefore \quad \sin x = \frac{\sqrt{\sec^2 x - 1}}{\sec x}, \tag{84}$$

and we already have,

$$\sin x = \frac{1}{\csc x}. \tag{85}$$

Formulas (81)–(85) express the sine in terms of the other functions. Similarly, each function in turn may be expressed in terms of each of the others. These transformations are left as exercises for the reader.

The relations developed in this article involve the functions of only one angle. In the next article we investigate the functions of combinations of more than one angle.

57. Sine and Cosine of the Sum of Two Angles. At first sight beginners sometimes think that sin $(x + y)$ should be equal to sin x + sin y, but we must remember that sin $(x + y)$ does not mean a product, $(\sin) \cdot (x + y)$. It means the sine of an angle which is the sum of the angles x and y. This is easily seen by taking specific numerical examples for x and y. Thus, let $x = 45°$ and $y = 30°$. Then, if it were correct to write sin $(x + y) = \sin x + \sin y$ we should have sin $(45° + 30°) = \sin 45° + \sin 30°$, or sin $75° = .7071 + .5000 = 1.2071$. But, from the table sin $75°$ is .9659 instead of 1.2071. Thus, we cannot say that sin $(x + y) = \sin x + \sin y$.

Similarly, we cannot write sin $2x = 2 \sin x$. If we could, then if $x = 30°$, we would have sin $(2 \times 30°) = 2 \sin 30°$. But $2 \times 30° = 60°$ and sin $30° = \frac{1}{2}$, and we would have sin $60° = 1$. But we know that sin $60° = .8660$ instead of 1.0000. Therefore, we cannot say that sin $2x = 2 \sin x$.

Similarly, also, we cannot write cos $(x + y) = \cos x + \cos y$, cos $2x = 2 \cos x$, etc. Of course, if x and y have known numerical values no such formula is necessary: it is only necessary to add $x + y$ and find the sine or cosine of the sum in the table, or to subtract and find the sine or cosine of the difference $x - y$ in the table. For other purposes, however, such formulas are necessary and useful, as previously pointed out and as already seen in article 52 in the case of sin $(\alpha - \theta)$. We now proceed to find the correct expressions for sin $(x + y)$ and cos $(x + y)$, where x and y may be any angles whatever.

In Fig. 97, let the arc APQ represent a portion of the unit circle of Fig. 42, article 14, and let $\angle AOP = x$, $\angle POQ = y$. Then $\angle AOQ = x + y$.

Draw $QR \perp OP$, QB and $RC \perp OA$, and $RS \parallel OA$. Then, as in Fig. 42 $QB = \sin \angle AOQ = \sin (x + y)$ and $OB = \cos \angle AOQ = \cos (x + y)$. We have to express QB and OB in terms of the functions of the separate angles x and y.

From the figure (Fig. 97) we have $QB = QS + SB$ and $SB = RC$, so $QB = QS + RC$. That is,

$$\sin (x + y) = \overline{RC} + \overline{QS}. \tag{86}$$

Also, $OB = OC - BC$ and $BC = RS$, so $OB = OC - RS$. That is,

$$\cos (x + y) = \overline{OC} - \overline{RS}. \tag{87}$$

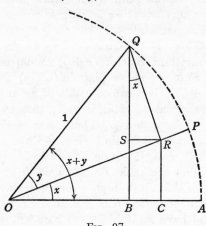

Fig. 97.

Now, $QB \perp OA$ and $QR \perp OP$; the two sides of $\angle RQS$ are, therefore, perpendicular to the sides of $\angle AOP = x$. According to (C), article 1, therefore, $\angle RQS = x$, as indicated in the figure. Then in right $\triangle QSR$, $\overline{RS}/\overline{QR} = \sin x$ and $\overline{QS}/\overline{QR} = \cos x$. Hence,

$$\overline{RS} = \sin x \cdot \overline{QR}, \quad \overline{QS} = \cos x \cdot \overline{QR}.$$

But in the unit circle $QR = \sin \angle POQ = \sin y$. Therefore,

$$\overline{RS} = \sin x \cdot \sin y. \tag{88}$$

$$\overline{QS} = \cos x \cdot \sin y. \tag{89}$$

Also, in right $\triangle OCR$, $\overline{RC}/\overline{OR} = \sin x$ and $\overline{CO}/\overline{OR} = \cos x$, or

$$\overline{RC} = \sin x \cdot \overline{OR}, \quad \overline{CO} = \cos x \cdot \overline{OR},$$

and in the unit circle $OR = \cos \angle POQ = \cos y$. Therefore,

$$\overline{RC} = \sin x \cdot \cos y, \tag{90}$$

$$\overline{OC} = \cos x \cdot \cos y. \tag{91}$$

Substituting in equation (86) the values of $\overline{RC}$ and $\overline{QS}$ given by (90) and (89), we have the result

$$\sin (x + y) = \sin x \cos y + \cos x \sin y. \tag{92}$$

Substituting in (87) the values of $\overline{OC}$ and $\overline{RS}$ given by (91) and (88), we have, finally,

$$\cos (x + y) = \cos x \cos y - \sin x \sin y. \qquad (93)$$

Formulas (92) and (93) are our desired results and are extremely important. We shall have frequent use for them in the remainder of this chapter.

58. Sine and Cosine of the Difference of Two Angles. To derive the formulas for $\sin (x - y)$ and $\cos (x - y)$ we proceed somewhat as in the preceding article. In the unit circle of Fig. 98 let $\angle AOP = x$, $\angle POQ = y$; then $\angle AOQ = x - y$.

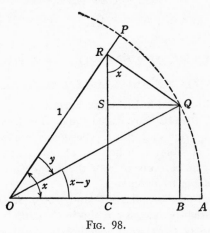

FIG. 98.

Draw $QR \perp OP$, QB and $RC \perp OA$, and $QS \parallel OA$. Then in the unit circle of Fig. 98

$$\sin (x - y) = QB = SC,$$
and
$$\cos (x - y) = OB = OC + CB.$$

But, $SC = RC - RS$ and $CB = QS$; therefore,

$$\sin (x - y) = \overline{RC} - \overline{RS}, \qquad (94)$$
$$\cos (x - y) = \overline{OC} + \overline{QS}. \qquad (95)$$

Also, in Fig. 98 as in Fig. 97, $\angle QRS = x$ and in right $\triangle QRS$ $\overline{RS}/\overline{RQ} = \cos x$, $\overline{QS}/\overline{RQ} = \sin x$. Hence,

$$\overline{RS} = \cos x \cdot \overline{RQ}, \quad \overline{QS} = \sin x \cdot \overline{RQ},$$

and in the unit circle $\overline{RQ} = \sin \angle POQ = \sin y$. Hence,

$$\overline{RS} = \cos x \cdot \sin y, \tag{96}$$

$$\overline{QS} = \sin x \cdot \sin y. \tag{97}$$

Again, in right $\triangle OCR$, $\overline{RC}/\overline{OR} = \sin \angle COR = \sin x$ and $\overline{OC}/\overline{OR} = \cos x$, hence,

$$\overline{RC} = \sin x \cdot \overline{OR}, \quad \overline{OC} = \cos x \cdot \overline{OR},$$

and in the unit circle $\overline{OR} = \cos \angle POQ = \cos y$. Therefore

$$\overline{RC} = \sin x \cdot \cos y, \tag{98}$$

$$\overline{OC} = \cos x \cdot \cos y. \tag{99}$$

Substituting (98) and (96) in (94), and (99), (97) in (95) we have the results

$$\sin (x - y) = \sin x \cos y - \cos x \sin y, \tag{100}$$

$$\cos (x - y) = \cos x \cos y + \sin x \sin y. \tag{101}$$

59. The Addition and Subtraction Formulas. The four formulas (92), (93) and (100), (101) are called the *addition formulas* and *subtraction formulas* of the sine and clsine. Because of their importance in the computation of tables, and because of the great number of other relations which can be derived from them, they are also called the *fundamental formulas* of trigonometry.

It is to be noted that formulas (92) and (100), (93) and (101) differ only in sign, and that both signs are plus in (92) and both are minus in (100) while opposite signs occur together in (93) and (101). Each pair (92), (100) and (93), (101) can, therefore, be combined in one formula with a double sign ("plus-or-minus," "minus-or-plus"), thus:

$$\sin (x \pm y) = \sin x \cos y \pm \cos x \sin y, \tag{102}$$

$$\cos (x \pm y) = \cos x \cos y \mp \sin x \sin y. \tag{103}$$

This is a concise and convenient form for writing and remembering the four fundamental formulas.

We shall in the remainder of this chapter derive a number of other formulas from these. For the present we shall show how easily one important formula we have already used can be obtained from (101). If we write (101) as

$$\cos x \cos y + \sin x \sin y = \cos (x - y),$$

and in it let $y = x$ it becomes

$$\cos x \cos x + \sin x \sin x = \cos (x - x).$$

But, $x - x = 0$ and $\cos 0 = 1$; also, $\cos x \cos x = \cos^2 x$ and $\sin x \sin x = \sin^2 x$. Therefore, the formula becomes

$$\cos^2 x + \sin^2 x = 1,$$

which is the same as formula (73).

As a check on the addition and subtraction formulas and an illustration and example of their use, let us put $x = 45°$, $y = 30°$. Then, (92) gives

$$\sin (45° + 30°) = \sin 45° \cos 30° + \cos 45° \sin 30°,$$

and using the values of the functions of 30, 45° from the tables,

$$\sin 75° = .7071 \times .8660 + .7071 \times .5000$$
$$= .61235 + .35355$$
$$= .9659,$$

which is the value given in the table for sin 75°.

Similarly, by (100),

$$\sin (45° - 30°) = .61235 - .35355,$$

or,

$$\sin 15° = .2588,$$

which is also the value given in the table.

In the same way we would find from (93) and (101),

$$\cos 75° = .2588, \quad \cos 15° = .9659,$$

which are of course correct, since $\sin 15° = \cos 75°$ and $\sin 75° = \cos 15°$ (75° and 15° being co-angles).

These values are the ones found in article 13 from the right triangle definitions of the functions, the values for 30° and 45° being already known. It is obvious now, however, that what was a somewhat laborious calculation in article 13 is very simply and easily performed with the aid of the addition and subtraction formulas.

If the values of the functions of a few small angles are known, then by repeated additions and subtractions and the use of these formulas, the functions of any angles can be calculated in the manner just illustrated. It is this fact which gives the fundamental formulas their great usefulness in computing the trigonometric tables.

60. Tangent of the Sum and Difference of Two Angles. Since for any angle whatever, $\tan = \dfrac{\sin}{\cos}$, then for the angle $(x + y)$ we have

$$\tan (x + y) = \frac{\sin (x + y)}{\cos (x + y)}.$$

Using formulas (92) and (93) in this fraction we have

$$\tan (x + y) = \frac{\sin x \cos y + \cos x \sin y}{\cos x \cos y - \sin x \sin y}. \tag{104}$$

The division of every term of both numerator and denominator of a fraction by the same quantity does not change the value of the fraction. We can, therefore, divide each term in numerator and denominator of the last fraction by the product $\cos x \cos y$. This gives

$$\tan (x + y) = \frac{\dfrac{\sin x \cos y}{\cos x \cos y} + \dfrac{\cos x \sin y}{\cos x \cos y}}{\dfrac{\cos x \cos y}{\cos x \cos y} - \dfrac{\sin x \sin y}{\cos x \cos y}}.$$

Cancelling like factors in numerator and denominator of each individual fraction, this becomes

$$\tan (x + y) = \frac{\dfrac{\sin x}{\cos x} + \dfrac{\sin y}{\cos y}}{1 - \dfrac{\sin x}{\cos x} \cdot \dfrac{\sin y}{\cos y}},$$

and remembering that $\sin/\cos = \tan$ we have finally,

$$\tan (x + y) = \frac{\tan x + \tan y}{1 - \tan x \tan y}, \tag{105}$$

which gives the tangent of the sum of any two angles in terms of their separate tangents. This is the addition formula for the tangent.

If we next substitute in the formula

$$\tan (x - y) = \frac{\sin (x - y)}{\cos (x - y)},$$

the previous formulas (100) and (101) we get formula (104) with signs changed. By the same reduction as that used above, therefore, we get

$$\tan (x - y) = \frac{\tan x - \tan y}{1 + \tan x \tan y}, \tag{106}$$

which is the tangent subtraction formula.

Since the formulas (105) and (106) are alike except in sign, they may be written together as

$$\tan (x \pm y) = \frac{\tan x \pm \tan y}{1 \mp \tan x \tan y}, \tag{107}$$

and in this form both are easily remembered.

61. Cotangent of the Sum and Difference of Two Angles. Since for any angle whatever, $\tan = 1/\cot$, we can write formula (105) in the form

$$\frac{1}{\cot (x + y)} = \frac{\dfrac{1}{\cot x} + \dfrac{1}{\cot y}}{1 - \dfrac{1}{\cot x} \cdot \dfrac{1}{\cot y}},$$

and by combining the fractions in the numerator and denominator of the expression on the right with the common denominator ($\cot x \cot y$) we get,

$$\frac{1}{\cot (x + y)} = \frac{\dfrac{\cot y + \cot x}{\cot x \cot y}}{\dfrac{\cot x \cot y - 1}{\cot x \cot y}} = \frac{\cot y + \cot x}{\cot x \cot y - 1}.$$

$$\therefore \quad \cot (x + y) = \frac{\cot x \cot y - 1}{\cot x + \cot y}, \tag{108}$$

the addition formula for the cotangent.

The cotangent subtraction formula is obtained in the same manner from (106) or by simply changing signs in (108).   It is

$$\cot (x - y) = \frac{\cot x \cot y + 1}{\cot x - \cot y}, \tag{109}$$

Formulas (106) and (109) may be written together as

$$\cot (x \pm y) = \frac{\cot x \cot y \mp 1}{\cot x \pm \cot y} \tag{110}$$

Formulas (102), (103), (107), (110) are the addition and subtraction formulas for the more commonly used functions sine, cosine, tangent, cotangent, respectively.   Similar formulas can be obtained for the secant and cosecant but these are but little used and will not be derived here.   Their derivation would be an interesting and instructive exercise for the reader.

62. Functions of Double Angles. Suppose that in the sine addition formula (92) the two angles are the same, that is, $y = x$. The formula then becomes

$$\sin (x + x) = \sin x \cos x + \sin x \cos x.$$

$$\therefore \quad \sin 2x = 2 \sin x \cos x. \tag{111}$$

Thus we have, *not* $\sin 2x = 2 \sin x$, but $\sin 2x = (2 \sin x) \cdot \cos x$, and this answers one of the questions considered in article 57. This formula may also be verified by giving x any numerical value. Thus, if $x = 30°$, $\sin x = \frac{1}{2}$, $\cos x = .8660$ and the formula gives

$$\sin 60° = 2 \times \tfrac{1}{2} \times .8660 = .8660,$$

which is correct, as seen in the tables. Similarly, if $x = 45°$,

$$\sin 2x = \sin 90° = 2 \times .7071 \times .7071 = 1.0000,$$

the known value of $\sin 90°$.

If it is desired to express this formula in terms of $\sin x$ alone, instead of sine and cosine, we have, from formula (73),

$$\cos x = \sqrt{1 - \sin^2 x}.$$

Hence,

$$\sin 2x = 2 \sin x \sqrt{1 - \sin^2 x}. \tag{112}$$

Form (111) is the simpler and more useful, however.

In order to obtain the formula for $\cos 2x$, let $y = x$ in formula (93). This gives

$$\cos (x + x) = \cos x \cos x - \sin x \sin x,$$

or,

$$\cos 2x = \cos^2 x - \sin^2 x. \tag{113}$$

This formula may be given in terms of either $\sin x$ or $\cos x$ alone and both forms are sometimes useful. By (73)

$$\sin^2 x = 1 - \cos^2 x, \text{ and } \cos^2 x = 1 - \sin^2 x.$$

Using each of these in turn in (113) we have

$$\cos 2x = \cos^2 x - (1 - \cos^2 x),$$

and

$$\cos 2x = (1 - \sin^2 x) - \sin^2 x.$$

$$\therefore \quad \left. \begin{array}{l} \cos 2x = 2 \cos^2 x - 1, \\ \cos 2x = 1 - 2 \sin^2 x. \end{array} \right\} \tag{114}$$

By putting $y = x$ in formulas (105) and (108) and collecting terms, they become, respectively,

$$\tan 2x = \frac{2 \tan x}{1 - \tan^2 x}, \tag{115}$$

$$\cot 2x = \frac{\cot^2 x - 1}{2 \cot x}. \tag{116}$$

63. Functions of Half Angles. The functions of half an angle are expressed in terms of the functions of the whole angle by means of the formulas of the preceding article.

From the second of formulas (114),

$$2 \sin^2 x = 1 - \cos 2x.$$

Dividing by 2 and taking the square root, this becomes

$$\sin x = \sqrt{\frac{1 - \cos 2x}{2}}.$$

If in this we put $2x = z$ then $x = \frac{1}{2}z$ and we have

$$\sin \tfrac{1}{2}z = \sqrt{\frac{1 - \cos z}{2}}. \tag{117}$$

Strictly speaking, a double sign ($\pm$) should be placed before a square root, and in (117) this would mean that $\sin \frac{1}{2}z$ would be positive or negative according to the quadrant in which it lies, as shown in Table III, article 36. If this is understood, it is not necessary to place the double sign before the square roots in any of the following function formulas.

In order to express $\sin \frac{1}{2}z$ in terms of $\sin z$ we have

$$\cos z = \sqrt{1 - \sin^2 z},$$

and (117) becomes

$$\sin \tfrac{1}{2}z = \left[\frac{1 - \sqrt{1 - \sin^2 z}}{2}\right]^{1/2}. \tag{118}$$

This formula is but little used.

From the first of formulas (114), $2 \cos^2 x = 1 + \cos 2x$. Hence, as above,

$$\cos x = \sqrt{\frac{1 + \cos 2x}{2}},$$

and if in this we put $2x = z$, then $x = \frac{1}{2}z$ and it becomes

$$\cos \tfrac{1}{2}z = \sqrt{\frac{1 + \cos z}{2}}. \tag{119}$$

Clearing formula (115) of fractions it is

$$\tan 2x(1 - \tan^2 x) = 2 \tan x.$$

Multiplying out and transposing, we get

$$\tan 2x \cdot \tan^2 x + 2 \tan x - \tan 2x = 0,$$

which is an algebraic quadratic equation with *tan x* as the unknown quantity and of the form

$$A \tan^2 x + B \tan x + C = 0,$$

where $A = \tan 2x$, $B = 2$, $C = -\tan 2x$. By the *quadratic formula* of algebra, the solution is

$$\tan x = \frac{-B \pm \sqrt{B^2 - 4AC}}{2A}.$$

Using the stated values of A, B, C, this gives

$$\tan x = \frac{-2 \pm \sqrt{4 + 4\tan^2 2x}}{2 \tan 2x}$$

$$= \frac{-1 \pm \sqrt{1 + \tan^2 2x}}{\tan 2x}$$

$$= -\frac{1}{\tan 2x} \pm \sqrt{\frac{1}{\tan^2 2x} + 1}.$$

Putting $2x = z$ and hence $x = \frac{1}{2}z$ as above, and using only the plus sign before the square root, this becomes finally

$$\tan \tfrac{1}{2}z = \sqrt{\frac{1}{\tan^2 z} + 1} - \frac{1}{\tan z}, \tag{120}$$

which gives $\tan \frac{1}{2}z$ in terms of tan z.

Clearing (116) of fractions and transposing, we get the quadratic equation

$$\cot^2 x - (2 \cot 2x) \cot x - 1 = 0,$$

which, when solved for cot x, gives

$$\cot x = \cot 2x \pm \sqrt{\cot^2 2x + 1}.$$

Again putting $2x = z$ and using only the plus sign we have finally

$$\cot \tfrac{1}{2}z = \cot z + \sqrt{1 + \cot^2 z}. \tag{121}$$

Formulas (118), (119), (120), (121) give the sine, cosine, tangent, cotangent, respectively, of half an angle in terms of the same function of the whole angle.

All four of the functions of the half angle may be very simply expressed in terms of the cosine of the whole angle. Thus, (117) and (119) already give $\sin \tfrac{1}{2}z$ and $\cos \tfrac{1}{2}z$ in terms of $\cos z$. From these we have

$$\tan \tfrac{1}{2}z = \frac{\sin \tfrac{1}{2}z}{\cos \tfrac{1}{2}z} = \frac{\sqrt{\dfrac{1 - \cos z}{2}}}{\sqrt{\dfrac{1 + \cos z}{2}}} = \sqrt{\dfrac{\dfrac{1 - \cos z}{2}}{\dfrac{1 + \cos z}{2}}}.$$

$$\therefore \quad \tan \tfrac{1}{2}z = \sqrt{\frac{1 - \cos z}{1 + \cos z}}. \tag{122}$$

From this, $\cot \tfrac{1}{2}z = \dfrac{1}{\tan \tfrac{1}{2}z} = \dfrac{1}{\sqrt{\dfrac{1 - \cos z}{1 + \cos z}}}.$

$$\therefore \quad \cot \tfrac{1}{2}z = \sqrt{\frac{1 + \cos z}{1 - \cos z}}. \tag{123}$$

64. Sums and Differences of Functions. There is one more set of formulas of some importance which are derived from the addition and subtraction formulas. Re-writing (92) and (100),

$$\sin (x + y) = \sin x \cos y + \cos x \sin y,$$
$$\sin (x - y) = \sin x \cos y - \cos x \sin y.$$

Adding these, $\left. \begin{array}{l} \sin (x + y) + \sin (x - y) = 2 \sin x \cos y; \\ \sin (x + y) - \sin (x - y) = 2 \cos x \sin y. \end{array} \right\} \tag{124}$

subtracting,

Now let

$$\left. \begin{array}{l} x + y = A, \\ x - y = B. \end{array} \right\} \tag{125}$$

Adding these, $2x = A + B;$

subtracting, $2y = A - B.$

$$\therefore \quad \left. \begin{array}{l} x = \tfrac{1}{2}(A + B), \\ y = \tfrac{1}{2}(A - B). \end{array} \right\} \tag{126}$$

Substituting (125) in the left side of (124), and (126) in the right side, formulas (124) become

$$\left.\begin{array}{l}\sin A + \sin B = 2 \sin \tfrac{1}{2}(A + B) \cos \tfrac{1}{2}(A - B), \\ \sin A - \sin B = 2 \cos \tfrac{1}{2}(A + B) \sin \tfrac{1}{2}(A - B).\end{array}\right\} \quad (127)$$

Re-writing (101) and (93),

$$\cos (x - y) = \cos x \cos y + \sin x \sin y,$$
$$\cos (x + y) = \cos x \cos y - \sin x \sin y.$$

Adding these, $\cos (x - y) + \cos (x + y) = 2 \cos x \cos y;$
subtracting, $\cos (x - y) - \cos (x + y) = 2 \sin x \sin y.$

Substituting (125) and (126) in these we have

$$\left.\begin{array}{l}\cos B + \cos A = 2 \cos \tfrac{1}{2}(A + B) \cos \tfrac{1}{2}(A - B), \\ \cos B - \cos A = 2 \sin \tfrac{1}{2}(A + B) \sin \tfrac{1}{2}(A - B).\end{array}\right\} \quad (128)$$

The formulas (127) and (128) are sometimes useful in converting sums and differences of functions into products of functions for logarithmic computation.

A very useful relation of this kind is obtained from the formulas (127). If the first of these two is divided by the second, there results

$$\frac{\sin A + \sin B}{\sin A - \sin B} = \frac{\sin \tfrac{1}{2}(A + B)}{\cos \tfrac{1}{2}(A + B)} \cdot \frac{\cos \tfrac{1}{2}(A - B)}{\sin \tfrac{1}{2}(A - B)}$$

But $\dfrac{\sin}{\cos} = \tan$ and $\dfrac{\cos}{\sin} = \cot = \dfrac{1}{\tan}$; therefore

$$\frac{\sin A + \sin B}{\sin A - \sin B} = \frac{\tan \tfrac{1}{2}(A + B)}{\tan \tfrac{1}{2}(A - B)}. \quad (129)$$

This is the relation which is used in article 41 in the derivation of the tangent law of the oblique triangle.

65. Functions of Triple Angles. It is frequently necessary in applied mathematics to express the functions of three times an angle in terms of the functions of the single angle, as was done in article 62 for a double angle. For $3x$, where x is, as before, any angle, this is easy; thus

$$\sin (3x) = \sin (2x + x)$$
$$= \sin 2x \cdot \cos x + \cos 2x \cdot \sin x,$$

by (92), with $2x$ replacing x and x replacing y. Now using (111) for $\sin 2x$ and the second of (114) for $\cos 2x$, we get

$$\sin 3x = 2 \sin x \cos x \cdot \cos x + (1 - 2 \sin^2 x) \sin x$$
$$= 2 \sin x \cos^2 x + \sin x - 2 \sin^3 x$$
$$= 2 \sin x(1 - \sin^2 x) + \sin x - 2 \sin^3 x$$
$$= 2 \sin x - 2 \sin^3 x + \sin x - 2 \sin^3 x;$$

$$\therefore \quad \sin 3x = 3 \sin x - 4 \sin^3 x. \tag{130}$$

Similarly, for the cosine of a triple angle,

$$\cos 3x = \cos (2x + x) = \cos 2x \cdot \cos x - \sin 2x \cdot \sin x$$
$$= (2 \cos^2 x - 1) \cos x - 2 \sin x \cos x \cdot \sin x$$
$$= 2 \cos^3 x - \cos x - 2 \sin^2 x \cdot \cos x$$
$$= 2 \cos^3 x - \cos x - 2(1 - \cos^2 x) \cos x$$
$$= 2 \cos^3 x - \cos x - 2 \cos x + 2 \cos^3 x;$$

$$\therefore \quad \cos 3x = 4 \cos^3 x - 3 \cos x. \tag{131}$$

Finally, for the tangent of a triple angle,

$$\tan 3x = \tan (2x + x) = \frac{\tan 2x + \tan x}{1 - \tan 2x \cdot \tan x},$$

and on replacing $\tan 2x$ with the fraction in formula (115),

$$\tan 3x = \frac{\left(\dfrac{2 \tan x}{1 - \tan^2 x} \right) + \tan x}{1 - \left(\dfrac{2 \tan x}{1 - \tan^2 x} \right) \cdot \tan x}$$

$$= \frac{\left[\dfrac{2 \tan x + \tan x(1 - \tan^2 x)}{1 - \tan^2 x} \right]}{\left[\dfrac{1 - \tan^2 x - 2 \tan x \cdot \tan x}{1 - \tan^2 x} \right]}$$

$$= \frac{2 \tan x + \tan x - \tan^3 x}{1 - \tan^2 x - 2 \tan^2 x};$$

$$\therefore \quad \tan 3x = \frac{3 \tan x - \tan^3 x}{1 - 3 \tan^2 x}. \tag{132}$$

Formulas (130), (131), (132) express the three chief functions of a triple angle ($3x$) in terms of those of the single angle x, and in them x may have any value at all, in degrees or radians. It is possible to derive similar formulas for the functions of $4x$, $5x$, etc., but these are not often needed and will not be included here.

66. Solution of Irreducible Case of Algebraic Cubic Equation.
Either of the formulas (130), (131) above may be used to obtain a
solution of a certain algebraic equation which cannot be solved by
purely algebraic methods. It is shown in algebra* that when, the
coefficients p and q in the equation $u^3 + p \cdot u + q = 0$, where u is an
unknown quantity to be found, are such that $(p/3)^3 + (q/2)^2$ is a
negative quantity the given equation cannot be solved for u by purely
algebraic methods.

It is also shown in algebra* that a complete cubic (third degree)
equation of the form

$$x^3 + ax^2 + bx + c = 0, \tag{133}$$

where a, b, c are known numbers, may always be reduced to the form

$$u^3 + p \cdot u + q = 0 \tag{134}$$

by substituting $x = u - (a/3)$ in (133), and hence that (133) is not
solvable when (134) is not. The equation (133) may also be reduced
to the form (134) at once by calculating the coefficients p and q
from a, b, c by the formulas

$$p = b - (a^2/3), \quad q = 2(a/3)^3 - b(a/3) + c, \tag{135}$$

and if a cubic equation is in the form (133) it must always be reduced
to (134) before attempting to solve it. When u is found from (134)
the unknown x of the original equation (133) is then given by

$$x = u - (a/3). \tag{136}$$

The solution of (134) will be outlined here, as the complete proofs
require certain principles which are only worked out in advanced
trigonometry and algebra.

For this purpose re-write formula (130) as

$$4 \sin^3 \theta - 3 \sin \theta + \sin (3\theta) = 0$$

or

$$\sin^3 \theta - \tfrac{3}{4} \sin \theta + \tfrac{1}{4} \sin (3\theta) = 0, \tag{137}$$

the symbol θ replacing x, to avoid confusion with the unknown x in
the equation (133). Now also replace u by mz in (134), where z is a
new unknown quantity and m is now to be determined. Then (134)
becomes $m^3z^3 + pmz + q = 0$, and on dividing by m^3

* See the author's "Algebra for the Practical Man," published by D. Van
Nostrand Co., New York.

$$z^3 + \left(\frac{p}{m^2}\right) z + \left(\frac{q}{m^3}\right) = 0. \tag{138}$$

On comparing equations (137) and (138) they are seen to be identical in form, with z corresponding to $\sin \theta$, and with the coefficients

$$\frac{p}{m^2} = \frac{-3}{4}, \quad \frac{1}{4} \sin (3\theta) = \frac{q}{m^3}. \tag{139}$$

From the first of these two formulas we find $m^2 = -(4p/3)$ and hence $m = 2\sqrt{-(p/3)}$, $1/m = \frac{1}{2}\sqrt{-(3/p)}$, and this in the second of formulas (139) gives

$$\frac{1}{4} \sin (3\theta) = \frac{q}{8} \left(\sqrt{-\frac{3}{p}}\right)^3, \quad \sin (3\theta) = \frac{q}{2} \left(\sqrt{-\frac{3}{p}}\right)^3.$$

Now

$$\frac{q}{2} \left(\sqrt{-\frac{3}{p}}\right)^3 = \sqrt{\left(\frac{q}{2}\right)^2 \cdot \left(-\frac{3}{p}\right)^3} = \sqrt{\left(\frac{q}{2}\right)^2 \Big/ \left(-\frac{p}{3}\right)^3},$$

and therefore

$$\sin (3\theta) = \sqrt{\left(\frac{q}{2}\right)^2 \Big/ \left(-\frac{p}{3}\right)^3}. \tag{140}$$

With p and q known in the equation (134) the quantity under the radical in (140) can be calculated, and so $\sin (3\theta)$ is known, and the angle (3θ) can be read from the table. The angle θ is then known, and in (137) and (138) $z = \sin \theta$. But the unknown quantity $u = mz = m \sin \theta$, and from (139) $m = 2\sqrt{-(p/3)}$. Therefore

$$u = \pm 2\sqrt{-(p/3)} \sin \theta. \tag{141}$$

It has been seen in Chapter VI that more than one angle can be found which have the same sine number, and it is shown in advanced trigonometry that there are three values of θ, differing by 120°, which satisfy (140) and (141) above. These are the acute angle, θ, $\theta + 120°$, and $\theta + 240°$, and when these are used in formula (141) they give *three* values of u. This result meets the requirement that an equation of the third degree must have three roots, as shown in algebra. The sign ($+$ or $-$) to be used before the radical in (141) is the same as that of q in the original equation (134).

The trigonometric method of solving the irreducible cubic equation may now be summarized from the preceding results in the form of a complete rule, as follows:

1. *Express the complete cubic in the form*

$$x^3 + ax^2 + bx + c = 0. \tag{133}$$

2. *In this substitute* $x = u - (a/3)$ *and simplify.   The reduced cubic is then*

$$u^3 + pu + q = 0. \tag{134}$$

3. *Using the values of p and q from this equation (with their signs) calculate the number*

$$D = \left(\frac{p}{3}\right)^3 + \left(\frac{q}{2}\right)^2.$$

4. *If the number D is positive or is equal to zero use the algebraic method to solve the equation.   If D is negative use the trigonometric method as follows:*

5. *Using the values of* $(p/3)^3$ *and* $(q/2)^2$ *and reversing the sign of* $p/3$, *from Step 3, calculate the quantity*

$$\sin(3\theta) = \sqrt{\left(\frac{q}{2}\right)^2 \Big/ \left(-\frac{p}{3}\right)^3}. \tag{140}$$

6. *Find from the table or otherwise the angle* (3θ) *whose sine is equal to this square root, and divide this angle by 3, obtaining the angle* θ.

7. *Using this value of* θ, *and also* $\theta + 120°$ *and* $\theta + 240°$, *the required values of the unknown quantity u are found by the three formulas*

$$\left.\begin{array}{l} u_1 = \pm 2\sqrt{-\dfrac{p}{3}} \sin \theta \\[2mm] u_2 = \pm 2\sqrt{-\dfrac{p}{3}} \sin (\theta - 120°) \\[2mm] u_3 = \pm 2\sqrt{-\dfrac{p}{3}} \sin (\theta - 240°) \end{array}\right\} \tag{141}$$

the sign before the radical being chosen the same as that of q in Step 2.

8. *If the original equation was* (134) *the values of u given by* (141) *are the required roots; if the original equation was* (133) *the required values of the unknown x are*

$$x_1 = u_1 - (a/3), \quad x_2 = u_2 - (a/3), \quad x_3 = u_3 - (a/3). \tag{136}$$

Example.   The following equation will now be solved by the rule just derived and stated.   Solve the equation

$$x^3 - 6x + 4 = 0.$$

Solution. Step 3. The equation being already in the reduced form (134), the coefficients are $p = -6$ and $q = 4$. Therefore $D = (-\frac{6}{3})^3 + (\frac{4}{2})^2 = (-2)^3 + (2)^2 = -8 + 4 = -4$.

5. As D is negative we now calculate

$$\sin (3\theta) = \sqrt{\frac{2^2}{-(-2)^3}} = \sqrt{\frac{4}{8}} = \sqrt{\frac{1}{2}} = \frac{1}{\sqrt{2}} = .7071.$$

6. The angle whose sine is $\dfrac{1}{\sqrt{2}}$ or .7071 is $3\theta = 45°$. Therefore $\theta = 15°$, $\theta + 120° = 135°$, and $\theta + 240° = 255°$.

7. As $q = +4$ and $-(p/3) = -(-6/3) = 2$, the values of u (or x) are now

$$x_1 = 2\sqrt{2} \sin \ 15° = 2 \times 1.414 \times .2588 = \quad 0.7321$$
$$x_2 = 2\sqrt{2} \sin 135° = 2 \times 1.414 \times .7071 = \quad 2.0000$$
$$x_3 = 2\sqrt{2} \sin 255° = 2 \times 1.414(-.9659) = -2.7321$$

8. As the given equation is in the reduced form these are the required answers.

67. Exercises. The formulas and relations among the trigonometric functions which have been developed in articles 56–65 of this chapter are of the greatest interest and beauty in themselves and are of the greatest importance and value in advanced or analytical trigonometry. We have seen something of the use of some of these results in previous chapters in deriving working formulas for solving triangles and technical problems, and one of the formulas of article 65 was used to obtain a solution of an equation which cannot be solved by the simple algebraic methods.

The following exercises are cubic equations of the forms discussed in article 66 and these are to be solved by the method described in the rule given there, which is illustrated by the example worked out above. If there is no x^2 term in the equation in any case it is already in the reduced form (134), but if there is a term containing x^2 in the equation as given it must be removed as described in the rule. Also, it should be noted that the equation as discussed and stated in the rule contains the x^3 term with coefficient 1, and if the coefficient is not unity (1) in any case the equation must first be divided (each term) by the actual coefficient of x^3 to get it into the form (133) so that the rule can be used.

Solve the following equations:

1. $x^3 - 31x - 30 = 0$.   6. $x^3 - 8x^2 + 19x - 12 = 0$.
2. $x^3 - 10x - 10 = 0$.   7. $3x^3 + 2x^2 - 3x - 2 = 0$.
3. $x^3 - 7x^2 - 14x + 48 = 0$.   8. $4x^3 - 109x + 210 = 0$.
4. $x^3 - 16x - 24 = 0$.   9. $x^3 + x = 2$.
5. $2x^3 + x^2 - 23x - 20 = 0$.   10. $x^3 + 5x^2 - 6x = 24$.

68. Examples in Analytical Trigonometry. In this section are presented some typical exercises of analytical trigonometry.

Example. Show that $\tan A = \dfrac{\sin A + \sin 2A}{1 + \cos A + \cos 2A}$

Solution. The following formulas are used.

$$\tan A = \frac{\sin A}{\cos A}, \quad \sin 2A = 2 \sin A \cos A, \quad \cos 2A = 2 \cos^2 A - 1.$$

Then $\dfrac{\sin A}{\cos A} = \dfrac{\sin A + 2 \sin A \cos A}{1 + \cos A + 2 \cos^2 A - 1}$

$$\frac{\sin A}{\cos A} = \frac{\sin A + 2 \sin A \cos A}{\cos A + 2 \cos^2 A}$$

$$\frac{\sin A}{\cos A} = \frac{\sin A(1 + 2 \cos A)}{\cos A(1 + 2 \cos A)}$$

Then by cancellation,

$$\frac{\sin A}{\cos A} = \frac{\sin A}{\cos A}$$

Example. Show that $\dfrac{2 \sin^2 x}{\sin 2x} + \cot x = \sec x \csc x$.

Solution. Make use of the following relationships.

$$\sin 2x = 2 \sin x \cos x, \quad \cot x = \frac{\cos x}{\sin x}, \quad \sec x = \frac{1}{\cos x}, \quad \csc x = \frac{1}{\sin x}.$$

Then $\dfrac{2 \sin^2 x}{\sin 2x} + \cot x = \sec x \csc x$

$$\frac{2 \sin^2 x}{2 \sin x \cos x} + \frac{\cos x}{\sin x} = \frac{1}{\cos x} \cdot \frac{1}{\sin x}$$

$$\frac{\sin x}{\cos x} + \frac{\cos x}{\sin x} = \frac{1}{\cos x \sin x}$$

$$\frac{\sin^2 x + \cos^2 x}{\cos x \sin x} = \frac{1}{\cos x \sin x}$$

$$\frac{1}{\cos x \sin x} = \frac{1}{\cos x \sin x}$$

Example. Prove the identity $\dfrac{\sin \theta}{1 + \cos \theta} + \dfrac{1 + \cos \theta}{\sin \theta} = 2 \cot \theta \sec \theta$.

Solution. $\dfrac{\sin \theta}{1 + \cos \theta} + \dfrac{1 + \cos \theta}{\sin \theta} = 2 \cot \theta \sec \theta$.

Combine the fractions on the left side of the equation to obtain

$$\frac{\sin^2 \theta + (1 + \cos \theta)^2}{(1 + \cos \theta) \sin \theta} = 2 \cot \theta \sec \theta$$

$$\frac{\sin^2 \theta + 1 + 2 \cos \theta + \cos^2 \theta}{(1 + \cos \theta) \sin \theta} = 2 \cot \theta \sec \theta.$$

Since $\sin^2 \theta + \cos^2 \theta = 1$, we have

$$\frac{2 + 2 \cos \theta}{(1 + \cos \theta) \sin \theta} = 2 \cot \theta \sec \theta$$

Since $\cot \theta = \dfrac{\cos \theta}{\sin \theta}$ and $\sec \theta = \dfrac{1}{\cos \theta}$, we have

$$\frac{2(1 + \cos \theta)}{(1 + \cos \theta) \sin \theta} = 2 \cdot \frac{\cos \theta}{\sin \theta} \cdot \frac{1}{\cos \theta}$$

Then by cancellation of $(1 + \cos \theta)$ and of $\cos \theta$,

$$\frac{2}{\sin \theta} = \frac{2}{\sin \theta}.$$

Example. Prove the identity $\dfrac{2 \tan x - \sin 2x}{2 \sin^2 x} = \tan x$.

Solution. Make use of the relationships

$$\tan x = \frac{\sin x}{\cos x} \quad \text{and} \quad \sin 2x = 2 \sin x \cos x$$

Multiply the numerator and denominator of the fraction on the left side of the equation by $\cos x$.

$$\frac{2 \sin x - 2 \sin x \cos^2 x}{2 \sin^2 x \cos x} = \frac{\sin x}{\cos x}$$

$$\frac{2 \sin x (1 - \cos^2 x)}{2 \sin^2 x \cos x} = \frac{\sin x}{\cos x}$$

Since $\sin^2 x + \cos^2 x = 1$, $1 - \cos^2 x = \sin^2 x$, and

$$\frac{2 \sin x \cdot \sin^2 x}{2 \sin^2 x \cos x} = \frac{\sin x}{\cos x}$$

Then cancelling $2 \sin^2 x$ in the fraction on the left

$$\frac{\sin x}{\cos x} = \frac{\sin x}{\cos x}$$

Example.   Prove the identity $\dfrac{\sin x + \sin 2x}{\sec x + 2} = \dfrac{\sin x}{\sec x}$

Solution.   Make use of the relationships

$$\sin 2x = 2 \sin x \cos x \quad \text{and} \quad \sec x = \frac{1}{\cos x}$$

Then $$\frac{\sin x + 2 \sin x \cos x}{\dfrac{1}{\cos x} + 2} = \frac{\sin x}{\dfrac{1}{\cos x}}$$

Multiply the numerator and denominator of each side of the equation by $\cos x$.

$$\frac{\sin x \cos x + 2 \sin x \cos^2 x}{1 + 2 \cos x} = \frac{\sin x \cos x}{1}$$

$$\frac{\sin x \cos x (1 + 2 \cos x)}{1 + 2 \cos x} = \sin x \cos x$$

Cancelling $(1 + 2 \cos x)$ from the fraction on the left

$$\sin x \cos x = \sin x \cos x$$

69. Exercises.
Prove the following identities.

1. $\dfrac{\cos 2x}{\sin x} + \dfrac{\sin 2x}{\cos x} = \csc x$

2. $\cos 2A = \dfrac{2 - \sec^2 A}{\sec^2 A}$

3. $\tan^2 x = \dfrac{1 - \cos 2x}{1 + \cos 2x}$

4. $\dfrac{\sin 2A}{\sin A} - \dfrac{\cos 2A}{\cos A} = \sec A$

5. $\dfrac{\sin (x + y)}{\cos x \cos y} = \tan x \tan y$

6. $\dfrac{\cos x}{1 - \tan x} + \dfrac{\sin x}{1 - \cot x} = \sin x + \cos x$

7. $\cot y + \dfrac{\sin y}{1 + \cos y} = \csc y$

8. $\left(\dfrac{\sec x + \csc x}{1 + \tan x}\right)^2 = \dfrac{\tan x + \cot x}{\tan x}$

REVIEW PROBLEMS

The following problems are designed to provide the reader with additional practice material.

1. Express $2 \cos x \csc 2x$ in terms of $\sin x$.

2. At a distance a from the foot of a tower, the angle of elevation x of the top is the complement of the angle of elevation of the top of a flagstaff on the tower. Show that the length of the flagstaff is $a(\cot x - \tan x)$.

3. From two points due west of an airplane at a distance d apart, the angles of elevation of the plane are x and y (x is greater than y). Prove that the distance s from the point on the ground directly beneath the plane to the nearest point of observation is given by the formula $s = \dfrac{d \cos x \sin y}{\sin (x - y)}$.

4. Prove that the area of any quadrilateral is equal to one-half the product of the two diagonals multiplied by the sine of the included angle.

5. In triangle ABC, angle $A = 42°$, angle $C = 115°$, and side $AC = 32.6$. Find, to the nearest tenth, the length of the altitude drawn from B to side AC extended.

6. Town B is 25.8 miles due east of town A and town C is farther south than either B or A. The distance from A to C is 29.4 miles and from B to C is 36.6 miles. Find, to the nearest degree, the direction of C from A.

7. Highway engineers plan to eliminate a curve in a road between two points A and B, which are on opposite sides of a hill, by building a straight tunnel through the hill from A to B. From a point C on top of the hill, 290 yards from A, the angles of depression of A and B are $28° 10'$ and $36° 20'$ respectively. If A and B are at the same level and if A, B, and C are in the same vertical plane, find the length of the proposed tunnel to the nearest ten yards.

8. Prove the identity: $\cot \theta - \dfrac{\cos 2\theta}{\sin \theta \cos \theta} = \tan \theta$

9. In the diagram below, angle R is a right angle, angle $TSR = \theta$ and angle TSP is twice angle TSR. If $PT = c$, and $SR = d$, prove that $\sin P = \dfrac{2d \sin \theta}{c}$.

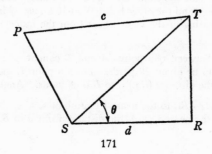

171

10. Two airports, A and B, are 600 miles apart. The bearing of B from A is 140° (S 40° E). Two planes leave points A and B simultaneously at speeds of 240 miles per hour and 300 miles per hour, respectively, and they both reach C in 5 hours. Find, to the nearest degree, the course (angle NAC) followed by the plane that took off from A. (Assume that there is no wind.)

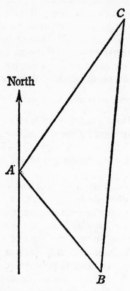

11. Prove the identity: $\dfrac{\sec x \sec y}{\tan x - \tan y} = \csc (x - y)$.

12. Point C is 70 miles directly east of point A. Point B is 60 miles from A and the bearing of B from A is 22° 20′ (N 22° 20′ E). Find, to the nearest mile, the distance from B to C.

13. Two boats start at the same time from the same place. One sails due south at 12 knots and the other S 72° W at 10 knots. Find, to the nearest degree, the bearing of the slower boat from the faster at the end of one hour.

14. The distance between two points A and B cannot be measured directly but is known to be about 20 yards. From a point C the distance to A is 82 yards and the distance from C to B is 64 yards. Angle CAB is 30° 40′.

    a. Find angle ABC to the nearest ten minutes.
    b. Find, to the nearest yard, the distance from A to B.

15. Airport A is 350 miles due north of airport B. Their radio stations receive signals of distress from ship C located S 72° E from A and N 46° E from B. How long will it take an airplane from A, traveling at the rate of 190 miles per hour, to reach the ship?

16. A triangular plot of ground measures 180 feet on one side and 240 feet on another side. The angle included between these sides is 72°. Find, to the nearest foot, the amount of fencing required to enclose the plot.

17. Point R is 100 miles directly east of point P. Point S is 90 miles from P, and the bearing of S from P is N 15° 40′ E. Find, to the nearest mile, the distance from S to R.

18. In the diagram below, AB represents a tower and CD a monument standing on level ground. From A, the angle of elevation of C is 42° 40′. From B the angle of elevation of C is 54° 30′. If the tower is 34 feet high, find to the nearest foot

    a. the distance BC.

    b. the height of the monument.

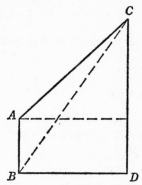

19. In right triangle ABC, C is the vertex of the right angle and D is any point in BC. Show that

    a. $DB = AC(\tan \angle CAB - \tan \angle CAD)$.

    b. $DB = \dfrac{AC \sin (\angle CAB - \angle CAD)}{\cos \angle CAB \cos \angle CAD}$.

20. A lighthouse at A is 8000 feet west of a lighthouse at B. From a ship the bearing of A is N 72° 20′ W and the bearing of B is N 65° 30′ E. Find the distance from the ship to the lighthouse at B to the nearest hundred feet.

21. Given acute triangle ABC with h the altitude on side C. Prove that

$$h = \frac{c}{\cot A + \cot B}.$$

22. In right triangle ADC, B is any point on AC and line BD is drawn. Derive a formula for DC in terms of AB, angle x and angle y.

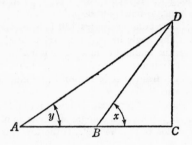

23. Point C is 4.4 miles from one end A of an island and 7.6 miles from the other end B. Angle ACB is 110°. Find, to the nearest mile, the length of the island.

24. Airfield B is directly north of airfield A. A plane takes off from A at noon and travels at a speed of 150 miles per hour in a direction N 20° 10' W. At the same time a second plane takes off from airfield B in a direction S 15° 40' W. At 2 p.m. the plane from A is directly above the plane from B. Find, to the nearest ten miles, the speed of the second plane.

25. In triangle ABC, $a \sin A = b \sin B$. Prove that triangle ABC is isosceles.

26. Prove the identity: $\dfrac{\sec A \tan A + \sec^2 A}{1 + (\sec A + \tan A)^2} = \frac{1}{2}$.

27. Show that, in right triangle ABC with right angle at C, the area is equal to each of the following:

$$\text{Area} = \tfrac{1}{2}bc \sin A$$
$$\text{Area} = \tfrac{1}{2}ac \cos A$$
$$\text{Area} = \tfrac{1}{2}c^2 \sin A \cos A.$$

28. Two land stations, A and B, equipped with radio beacons, are 150 miles apart. B is due north of A. A ship in a dense fog communicates with both stations in order to determine its position. If the ship is N 65° 30'E from A and S 34° 30' from B, find, correct to the nearest mile, how far it is from A.

29. A building stands on the top of a hill whose side has a uniform inclination of α with the horizontal. At a distance of k from the foot of the building, measured down the hill, the building subtends an angle of β. Find the height h of the building.

30. In triangle ABC, prove that

$$a = \frac{c \sin A}{\sin (A + B)}.$$

31. A tunnel extends in a straight line between two points, A and B, on opposite sides of a hill. At a point C 820 feet from A and 640 feet from B the angle subtended by the line AB is 78°. Find, correct to the nearest foot, the length of the tunnel.

32. The captain of a ship which is sailing north at the rate of 15 miles per hour observes a lighthouse N 35° W. One hour later he observes this lighthouse to be S 70° W. Find, correct to the nearest mile, the distance of the ship from the lighthouse at the second observation.

33. Prove that in right triangle ABC, with right angle at C, $\cos 2A = \cos^2 A - \sin^2 A$.

34. Two observers, 5280 feet apart on a straight horizontal road observe a balloon between them directly above the road. At the points of observation the angles of elevation of the balloon are 60° and 75°. Find, correct to the nearest foot, the height of the balloon.

35. Two roads intersect at an angle of 65° 20′. A triangular corner lot has a frontage of 125 feet on one road and 168 feet on the other road. Find the area of the lot correct to the nearest square foot.

36. In right triangle ABC, C is the right angle. Prove that $\tan \frac{1}{2}A = \sqrt{\dfrac{c - b}{c + b}}$.

37. From two points due west of a balloon, the angles of elevation of the balloon are x and y $(x > y)$. The distance between the two points is d. Show that the distance s from the point on the ground directly beneath the balloon to the nearer point of observation is given by the formula
$$s = \frac{d \cos x \sin y}{\sin (x - y)}.$$

38. A merchant vessel sails from a certain port directly east at 12 knots. A submarine is 10 nautical miles (1 knot = 1 nautical mile per hour) southwest from this port. At what rate must the submarine proceed in order to overtake the vessel in 2 hours?

39. Prove that the area K of a regular polygon of n sides inscribed in a circle of radius R is given by the formula
$$K = nR^2 \sin \frac{180°}{n} \cdot \cos \frac{180°}{n}.$$

40. An artillery range spotter is flying at an altitude of h feet. He observes that a gun G and its target T, both in the same horizontal plane, are due west of his position, the target being at the greater distance. The angles of depression of the gun and the target are x and y, respectively. Derive a formula for the range r, that is, the distance GT.

41. When the altitude (angle of elevation) of the sun is 32° 20′, the shadow of a radio tower is 60 feet longer than when the altitude of the sun is 44° 40′. Find, correct to the nearest foot, the height of the tower.

42. A valley is crossed by a bridge AB whose length is d; C is a point in the valley directly below the bridge. The angles of depression of C at A and

B are s and t, as shown in the drawing. In terms of s, t, and d, derive a formula for the height h of the bridge above C.

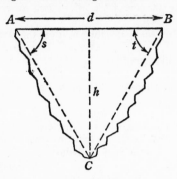

43. A person standing at a distance a from a tower surmounted by a spire observes the tower and the spire to subtend the same angle θ, as shown in the drawing. If b is the known height of the tower, show that the height h of the spire is given by the formula

$$h = \frac{b(a^2 + b^2)}{a^2 - b^2}.$$

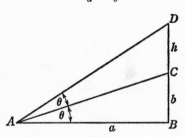

44. Using the law of cosines, prove that if two medians of a triangle are equal, the triangle is isosceles.

45. From a point d feet above level ground, the angle of elevation of the top of a building is x and the angle of depression of the foot of the building is y. Show that the height h of the building is given by the formula

$$h = \frac{d(\tan x + \tan y)}{\tan y}.$$

46. If A, B, and C are the angles of any triangle prove that $\sin A \cos B + \cos A \sin B = \sin C$.

47. The two parallel sides of a trapezoid are a and b, and the angles formed by the non-parallel sides at the two ends of one of the parallel sides are, respectively, A and B. Find the lengths of the non-parallel sides.

48. Derive a formula for $\cos 4A$ in terms of $\cos A$.

49. If the apothem of a regular polygon of n sides is a and an interior angle of the polygon is 2θ, derive a formula for the area of the polygon in terms of n, a, and θ.

50. From a point C at sea level, the angle of elevation of a mountain peak B is 30°. An aviator at A, 4325 feet directly above C, finds that $\angle BAC$ is 43°. Find, correct to the nearest foot, the height of the mountain peak above sea level.

ANSWERS TO EXERCISES
AND PROBLEMS

Article 6, Page 26

1. 87°44′; 31°10′.
2. 137°14′; 38°18′.
3. 136°48′, 274°12′, 15°12′, 30°28′.
4. 70°37′, 47°11′.
5. .8225, .32375, 2.2015.
6. 91°41′, 137°31′, 120°, 153°.
7. $\frac{7}{12}\pi$ = 1.83260, $\frac{2}{3}\pi$ = 2.09440, $\frac{3}{4}\pi$ = 2.35619, $\frac{5}{6}\pi$ = 2.61799 rad.

Ex.	r	θ	s	u
8.			20 in.	100 sq. in.
9.		$\frac{3}{4}$ rad.		600 sq. cm.
10.		8 rad.	34 ft.	
11.	8 in.			14 sq. in.
12.	2.57 ft.		7.74 ft.	
13.	8.93 cm.	1.062 rad.		
14.			296 in.	83,600 sq. in.
15.		1.52 rad.		33,495 sq. rd.
16.		4.03 rad.	28.3 ft.	
17.	1.445 yd.			1.88 sq. yd.
18.	9.30 m.		6.15 m.	
19.	9.05 in.	2.03 rad.		

20. 5.196 ft.
21. 44.1 ft., 1103 sq. ft.
22. 0.4369 mi. or 2307 ft.
23. 129 miles.
24. $C = 101°\,55′$.
25. Angle at center = 132° = 3.30383 rad. Each other angle = 24° = 0.41888 rad.

Article 10, Page 38

1. $a = 8$, $\sin A = .80$, $\cos A = .60$, $\tan A = 1.33$
2. $c = 39$, $\sin A = .38$, $\cos A = .92$, $\tan A = .42$
3. $b = 24$, $\sin A = .28$, $\cos A = .96$, $\tan A = .29$
4. $c = 34$, $\sin A = .47$, $\cos A = .88$, $\tan A = .53$
5. $b = 24$, $\sin A = .28$, $\cos A = .96$, $\tan A = .42$
6. $a = 9$, $\sin A = .22$, $\cos A = .98$, $\tan A = .23$

Article 26, Page 62

1. $A = 40° 52'$
  $a = 22.7$
  $b = 26.2$
2. $A = 34° 40'$
  $B = 55° 20'$
  $b = 231$
3. $A = 61° 12'$
  $B = 28° 48'$
  $c = 5.50$
4. $B = 26° 29'$
  $a = 273$
  $b = 136$
5. $A = 50° 30'$
  $B = 39° 30'$
  $a = 285$
6. $A = 42° 5'$
  $B = 47° 55'$
  $c = 97$
7. $A = 20° 36'$
  $b = 9.65$
  $c = 10.3$

8. $B = 29° 4'$
  $b = 19$
  $c = 38.9$
9. $B = 49° 47'$
  $a = 520$
  $c = 804$
10. $A = 34° 43'$
  $a = 111$
  $c = 195$
11. $A = 51° 18'$
  $B = 38° 42'$
  $c = 6.150$
12. $A = 44° 15'$
  $a = .005690$
  $b = .005841$
13. $A = 54° 42'$
  $b = 199.6$
  $c = 344.3$
14. $B = 38° 56'$
  $b = 3.553$
  $c = 5.653$

15. $A = 37° 41'$
  $B = 53° 19'$
  $c = 1633$
16. $B = 50° 26'$
  $a = 45.96$
  $b = 55.62$
17. $A = 46° 12'$
  $a = 53.12$
  $c = 73.59$
18. $A = 44° 35'$
  $b = 2.221$
  $c = 3.119$
19. $A = 56° 3'$
  $B = 33° 57'$
  $b = 48.32$
20. $A = 53° 30'$
  $B = 36° 30'$
  $a = 24.67$
21. $A = 1° 22'$
  $B = 88° 38'$
  $b = 91.89'$

Article 27, Page 64

1. 2750.
2. 805.9
3. 294.

4. 40.13.
5. 74.37.
6. 74.4.

7. 1262.
8. 82.02.
9. 182.2.

Article 32, Page 85

1. 3270 ft.
2. 37° 34'.
3. 200 ft.
4. 78.35 ft.
5. 1.43 mi.
6. 43.1 ft.
7. 685.9 ft.
8. 654.26 ft.

9. $h = 500$, $s = 625$,
  $w = 750$ ft.
10. 238,500 mi.
11. 2126 mi.
12. 1 mile.
13. 2.873 in.
14. 5.16 mi.
15. 35.16 ft.
16. 218.24 in.

17. $C = 2r \sin (\tfrac{1}{2}\theta)$.
18. 1.202 in.
19. $\theta = 14° 54'$; $s = 7.02$.
20. 18 in.
21. $90\tfrac{1}{2}°$; 84.5 ft.
22. 9760 ft.
23. 24,850 lb.
24. 1594 gal.
25. 616.6 sq. in.

Article 48, Page 119

1. $b = 209$
   $c = 240$
   $C = 123° 24'$
2. $A = 53° 30'$
   $B = 77° 30'$
   $c = 26.3$
3. $B = 77°$
   $a = 631$
   $c = 930$
4. $A = 55° 20'$
   $B = 92° 40'$
   $C = 32° 0'$
5. $B = 116 °20'$
   $C = 30° 30'$
   $a = 53.7$
6. $B = 56° 56'$
   $b = 56.9$
   $c = 53.6$
7. $C = 35° 4'$
   $b = 57.7$
   $c = 46.9$
8. $A = 40° 27'$
   $C = 15° 33'$
   $b = 399$

9. $A = 32° 11'$
   $B = 136° 24'$
   $C = 11° 25'$
10. $A = 60° 51'$
    $B = 73° 2'$
    $C = 46° 7'$
11. $A = 31°$
    $B = 90°$
    $a = 83.9$
12. $C = 55° 20'$
    $b = 56.7$
    $c = 66.4$
13. $A = 21° 6.8'$
    $B = 19° 46.5'$
    $c = 1.325$
14. $A = 37° 15\frac{3}{4}'$
    $B = 116° 4\frac{3}{4}'$
    $C = 26° 39\frac{1}{2}'$
15. $B = 60° 45'$
    $C = 39° 15'$
    $a = 984.8$
16. $B = 57° 24'$
    $C = 2° 1'$
    $c = .3853$

17. $A = 108° 50'$
    $b = 53.28$
    $c = 47.32$
18. $B = 56° 56'$
    $b = 5686$
    $c = 5358$
19. $C = 47° 14'$
    $a = 1341$
    $b = 1114$
20. $A = 53° 5'$
    $C = 16° 42'$
    $a = 37.46$
21. $A = 46° 27'$
    $B = 57° 11'$
    $C = 75° 52'$
22. $A = 51° 15'$
    $B = 56° 30'$
    $c = 95.24$
23. $A = 57° 24'$
    $C = 83° 9'$
    $b = 4501$
24. $A = 74° 23'$
    $B = 59° 2'$
    $C = 46° 35'$

25. 30.39.   26. 35.06.   27. 615.0.   28. 64.89.   29. 2.02.   30. 3864.

Article 54, Page 145

1. 56.56 ft.
2. 51.6 ft.
3. 431 ft.
4. 5.003; 2.339 in.
5. 295 ft.
6. 10 ft. per min.
7. 729.7 yds.
8. 85° 37' N. of W.
9. 63° 54'.
10. 18.8; 40.9 ft.
11. Sixty degrees.
12. 12.43 in.
13. 119.3 ft.
14. 0.3 lb.
15. 13 in.
16. $7.81.
17. 152.4 yds.; 1.475 A.
18. $49\frac{1}{4}$ min.
19. 16,368 sq. ft.; 339 ft.
20. 49° 25' S. of W.
21. 29.2 mi.
22. 91.76 ft.
23. 5.545 mi.
24. 15 ft.
25. $1735.

Article 67, Page 167

1. $x = -1, -5, 6.$
2. $x = -1.152, -2.424, 3.577.$
3. $x = 2, 8, -3.$
4. $x = 4.606, -1.914, -2.692.$
5. $x = 1, 2.5, -4.$
6. $x = 1, 3, 4.$

7. $x = 1, -1, -0.6667$.
8. $x = 2.5, 3.5, -6$.

9. $x = 1, 0.823, -1.823$.
10. $x = 2.2749, -2.0000, -5.2749$.

Review Problems, Page 171

1. $\dfrac{1}{\sin x}$.

5. 52.3.

6. 83°.

7. 470 yards.

10. 32°.

12. 73 miles.

13. N 47° W.

14. a. 140° 0'.
    b. 21 yards.

15. 1.5 hours.

16. 670 feet.

17. 115 miles.

18. a. 122 feet.
    b. 99 feet.

20. 3,600 feet.

22. $DC = \dfrac{AB}{\cot y - \cot x}$.

23. 10 miles.

24. 190 miles per hour.

28. 86 miles

29. $h = \dfrac{k \sin B}{\cos (\alpha + B)}$.

31. 929 feet.

32. 9 miles.

34. 6,246 feet.

35. 9,542 square feet.

38. 14.5 miles per hour.

40. $r = h(\cot y - \cot x)$.

41. 106 feet.

42. $h = \dfrac{d}{\cot t + \cot s}$.

47. $\dfrac{(a - b) \sin A}{\sin (A + B)}$ and $\dfrac{(a - b) \sin B}{\sin (A + B)}$.

48. $8 \cos^4 A - 8 \cos^2 A + 1$.

49. Area $= \dfrac{a^2 n}{\tan \theta}$.

50. 1,394 feet.

TABLES

IMPORTANT CONSTANTS FOR ANGLE CONVERSIONS

$$\pi = 3.14159265, \quad \pi \text{ radians} = 180 \text{ degrees}$$

$$1 \text{ radian} = \frac{180}{\pi} = 57.2957795°$$

$$= 57° \ 17' \ 44.806''$$

or,

$$1 \text{ radian} = 57° \ 17' \ 45''$$

$$1 \text{ degree} = \frac{\pi}{180} = 0.01745329 \text{ radian}$$

$$1 \text{ minute} = 0.00029089 \text{ radian}$$
$$1 \text{ second} = 0.00000485 \text{ radian}$$

DEGREES, MINUTES AND SECONDS TO RADIANS

Deg	Rad	Min	Rad	Sec	Rad
1	0.01745 33	1	0.00029 09	1	0.00000 48
2	0.03490 66	2	0.00058 18	2	0.00000 97
3	0.05235 99	3	0.00087 27	3	0.00001 45
4	0.06981 32	4	0.00116 36	4	0.00001 94
5	0.08726 65	5	0.00145 44	5	0.00002 42
6	0.10471 98	6	0.00174 53	6	0.00002 91
7	0.12217 30	7	0.00203 62	7	0.00003 39
8	0.13962 63	8	0.00232 71	8	0.00003 88
9	0.15707 96	9	0.00261 80	9	0.00004 36
10	0.17453 29	10	0.00290 89	10	0.00004 85
20	0.34906 59	20	0.00581 78	20	0.00009 70
30	0.52359 88	30	0.00872 66	30	0.00014 54
40	0.69813 17	40	0.01163 55	40	0.00019 39
50	0.87266 46	50	0.01454 44	50	0.00024 24
60	1.04719 76	60	0.01745 33	60	0.00029 09
70	1.22173 05				
80	1.39626 34				
90	1.57079 63				

RADIANS TO DEGREES, MINUTES AND SECONDS

	Radians	Tenths	Hundredths	Thousandths	Ten-thousandths
1	57° 17′ 44″.8	5° 43′ 46″.5	0° 34′ 22″.6	0° 3′ 26″.3	0° 0′ 20″.6
2	114° 35′ 29″.6	11° 27′ 33″.0	1° 8′ 45″.3	0° 6′ 52″.5	0° 0′ 41″.3
3	171° 53′ 14″.4	17° 11′ 19″.4	1° 43′ 07″.9	0° 10′ 18″.8	0° 1′ 01″.9
4	229° 10′ 59″.2	22° 55′ 05″.9	2° 17′ 30″.6	0° 13′ 45″.1	0° 1′ 22″.5
5	286° 28′ 44″.0	28° 38′ 52″.4	2° 51′ 53″.2	0° 17′ 11″.3	0° 1′ 43″.1
6	343° 46′ 28″.8	34° 22′ 38″.9	3° 26′ 15″.9	0° 20′ 37″.6	0° 2′ 03″.8
7	401° 4′ 13″.6	40° 6′ 25″.4	4° 0′ 38″.5	0° 24′ 03″.9	0° 2′ 24″.4
8	458° 21′ 58″.4	45° 50′ 11″.8	4° 35′ 01″.2	0° 27′ 30″.1	0° 2′ 45″.0
9	515° 39′ 43″.3	51° 33′ 58″.3	5° 9′ 23″.8	0° 30′ 56″.4	0° 3′ 05″.6

183

	0	1	2	3	4	5	6	7	8	9	1 2 3	4 5 6	7 8 9
10	0000	0043	0086	0128	0170	0212	0253	0294	0334	0374			
11	0414	0453	0492	0531	0569	0607	0645	0682	0719	0755	4 8 11	15 19 23	26 30 34
12	0792	0828	0864	0899	0934	0969	1004	1038	1072	1106	3 7 10	14 17 21	24 28 31
13	1139	1173	1206	1239	1271	1303	1335	1367	1399	1430	3 6 10	13 16 19	23 26 29
14	1461	1492	1523	1553	1584	1614	1644	1673	1703	1732	3 6 9	12 15 18	21 24 27
15	1761	1790	1818	1847	1875	1903	1931	1959	1987	2014	3 6 8	11 14 17	20 22 25
16	2041	2068	2095	2122	2148	2175	2201	2227	2253	2279	3 5 8	11 13 16	18 21 24
17	2304	2330	2355	2380	2405	2430	2455	2480	2504	2529	2 5 7	10 12 15	17 20 22
18	2553	2577	2601	2625	2648	2672	2695	2718	2742	2765	2 5 7	9 12 14	16 19 21
19	2788	2810	2833	2856	2878	2900	2923	2945	2967	2989	2 4 7	9 11 13	16 18 20
20	3010	3032	3054	3075	3096	3118	3139	3160	3181	3201	2 4 6	8 11 13	15 17 19
21	3222	3243	3263	3284	3304	3324	3345	3365	3385	3404	2 4 6	8 10 12	14 16 18
22	3424	3444	3464	3483	3502	3522	3541	3560	3579	3598	2 4 6	8 10 12	14 15 17
23	3617	3636	3655	3674	3692	3711	3729	3747	3766	3784	2 4 6	7 9 11	13 15 17
24	3802	3820	3838	3856	3874	3892	3909	3927	3945	3962	2 4 5	7 9 11	12 14 16
25	3979	3997	4014	4031	4048	4065	4082	4099	4116	4133	2 3 5	7 9 10	12 14 15
26	4150	4166	4183	4200	4216	4232	4249	4265	4281	4298	2 3 5	7 8 10	11 13 15
27	4314	4330	4346	4362	4378	4393	4409	4425	4440	4456	2 3 5	6 8 9	11 13 14
28	4472	4487	4502	4518	4533	4548	4564	4579	4594	4609	2 3 5	6 8 9	11 12 14
29	4624	4639	4654	4669	4683	4698	4713	4728	4742	4757	1 3 4	6 7 9	10 12 13
30	4771	4786	4800	4814	4829	4843	4857	4871	4886	4900	1 3 4	6 7 9	10 11 13
31	4914	4928	4942	4955	4969	4983	4997	5011	5024	5038	1 3 4	6 7 8	10 11 12
32	5051	5065	5079	5092	5105	5119	5132	5145	5159	5172	1 3 4	5 7 8	9 11 12
33	5185	5198	5211	5224	5237	5250	5263	5276	5289	5302	1 3 4	5 6 8	9 10 12
34	5315	5328	5340	5353	5366	5378	5391	5403	5416	5428	1 3 4	5 6 8	9 10 11
35	5441	5453	5465	5478	5490	5502	5514	5527	5539	5551	1 2 4	5 6 7	9 10 11
36	5563	5575	5587	5599	5611	5623	5635	5647	5658	5670	1 2 4	5 6 7	8 10 11
37	5682	5694	5705	5717	5729	5740	5752	5763	5775	5786	1 2 3	5 6 7	8 9 10
38	5798	5809	5821	5832	5843	5855	5866	5877	5888	5899	1 2 3	5 6 7	8 9 10
39	5911	5922	5933	5944	5955	5966	5977	5988	5999	6010	1 2 3	4 5 7	8 9 10
40	6021	6031	6042	6053	6064	6075	6085	6096	6107	6117	1 2 3	4 5 6	8 9 10
41	6128	6138	6149	6160	6170	6180	6191	6201	6212	6222	1 2 3	4 5 6	7 8 9
42	6232	6243	6253	6263	6274	6284	6294	6304	6314	6325	1 2 3	4 5 6	7 8 9
43	6335	6345	6355	6365	6375	6385	6395	6405	6415	6425	1 2 3	4 5 6	7 8 9
44	6435	6444	6454	6464	6474	6484	6493	6503	6513	6522	1 2 3	4 5 6	7 8 9
45	6532	6542	6551	6561	6571	6580	6590	6599	6609	6618	1 2 3	4 5 6	7 8 9
46	6628	6637	6646	6656	6665	6675	6684	6693	6702	6712	1 2 3	4 5 6	7 7 8
47	6721	6730	6739	6749	6758	6767	6776	6785	6794	6803	1 2 3	4 5 5	6 7 8
48	6812	6821	6830	6839	6848	6857	6866	6875	6884	6893	1 2 3	4 4 5	6 7 8
49	6902	6911	6920	6928	6937	6946	6955	6964	6972	6981	1 2 3	4 4 5	6 7 8
50	6990	6998	7007	7016	7024	7033	7042	7050	7059	7067	1 2 3	3 4 5	6 7 8
51	7076	7084	7093	7101	7110	7118	7126	7135	7143	7152	1 2 3	3 4 5	6 7 8
52	7160	7168	7177	7185	7193	7202	7210	7218	7226	7235	1 2 2	3 4 5	6 7 7
53	7243	7251	7259	7267	7275	7284	7292	7300	7308	7316	1 2 2	3 4 5	6 6 7
54	7324	7332	7340	7348	7356	7364	7372	7380	7388	7396	1 2 2	3 4 5	6 6 7

	0	1	2	3	4	5	6	7	8	9	1 2 3	4 5 6	7 8 9
55	7404	7412	7419	7427	7435	7443	7451	7459	7466	7474	1 2 2	3 4 5	5 6 7
56	7482	7490	7497	7505	7513	7520	7528	7536	7543	7551	1 2 2	3 4 5	5 6 7
57	7559	7566	7574	7582	7589	7597	7604	7612	7619	7627	1 2 2	3 4 5	5 6 7
58	7634	7642	7649	7657	7664	7672	7679	7686	7694	7701	1 1 2	3 4 4	5 6 7
59	7709	7716	7723	7731	7738	7745	7752	7760	7767	7774	1 1 2	3 4 4	5 6 7
60	7782	7789	7796	7803	7810	7818	7825	7832	7839	7846	1 1 2	3 4 4	5 5 6
61	7853	7860	7868	7875	7882	7889	7896	7903	7910	7917	1 1 2	3 4 4	5 6 6
62	7924	7931	7938	7945	7952	7959	7966	7973	7980	7987	1 1 2	3 3 4	5 6 6
63	7993	8000	8007	8014	8021	8028	8035	8041	8048	8055	1 1 2	3 3 4	5 5 6
64	8062	8069	8075	8082	8089	8096	8102	8109	8116	8122	1 1 2	3 3 4	5 5 6
65	8129	8136	8142	8149	8156	8162	8169	8176	8182	8189	1 1 2	3 3 4	5 5 6
66	8195	8202	8209	8215	8222	8228	8235	8241	8248	8254	1 1 2	3 3 4	5 5 6
67	8261	8267	8274	8280	8287	8293	8299	8306	8312	8319	1 1 2	3 3 4	5 5 6
68	8325	8331	8338	8344	8351	8357	8363	8370	8376	8382	1 1 2	3 3 4	4 5 6
69	8388	8395	8401	8407	8414	8420	8426	8432	8439	8445	1 1 2	2 3 4	4 5 6
70	8451	8457	8463	8470	8476	8482	8488	8494	8500	8506	1 1 2	2 3 4	4 5 6
71	8513	8519	8525	8531	8537	8543	8549	8555	8561	8567	1 1 2	2 3 4	4 5 5
72	8573	8579	8585	8591	8597	8603	8609	8615	8621	8627	1 1 2	2 3 4	4 5 5
73	8633	8639	8645	8651	8657	8663	8669	8675	8681	8686	1 1 2	2 3 4	4 5 5
74	8692	8698	8704	8710	8716	8722	8727	8733	8739	8745	1 1 2	2 3 4	4 5 5
75	8751	8756	8762	8768	8774	8779	8785	8791	8797	8802	1 1 2	2 3 3	4 5 5
76	8808	8814	8820	8825	8831	8837	8842	8848	8854	8859	1 1 2	2 3 3	4 5 5
77	8865	8871	8876	8882	8887	8893	8899	8904	8910	8915	1 1 2	2 3 3	4 4 5
78	8921	8927	8932	8938	8943	8949	8954	8960	8965	8971	1 1 2	2 3 3	4 4 5
79	8976	8982	8987	8993	8998	9004	9009	9015	9020	9025	1 1 2	2 3 3	4 4 5
80	9031	9036	9042	9047	9053	9058	9063	9069	9074	9079	1 1 2	2 3 3	4 4 5
81	9085	9090	9096	9101	9106	9112	9117	9122	9128	9133	1 1 2	2 3 3	4 4 5
82	9138	9143	9149	9154	9159	9165	9170	9175	9180	9186	1 1 2	2 3 3	4 4 5
83	9191	9196	9201	9206	9212	9217	9222	9227	9232	9238	1 1 2	2 3 3	4 4 5
84	9243	9248	9253	9258	9263	9269	9274	9279	9284	9289	1 1 2	2 3 3	4 4 5
85	9294	9299	9304	9309	9315	9320	9325	9330	9335	9340	1 1 2	2 3 3	4 4 5
86	9345	9350	9355	9360	9365	9370	9375	9380	9385	9390	1 1 2	2 3 3	4 4 5
87	9395	9400	9405	9410	9415	9420	9425	9430	9435	9440	0 1 1	2 2 3	3 4 4
88	9445	9450	9455	9460	9465	9469	9474	9479	9484	9489	0 1 1	2 2 3	3 4 4
89	9494	9499	9504	9509	9513	9518	9523	9528	9533	9538	0 1 1	2 2 3	3 4 4
90	9542	9547	9552	9557	9562	9566	9571	9576	9581	9586	0 1 1	2 2 3	3 4 4
91	9590	9595	9600	9605	9609	9614	9619	9624	9628	9633	0 1 1	2 2 3	3 4 4
92	9638	9643	9647	9652	9657	9661	9666	9671	9675	9680	0 1 1	2 2 3	3 4 4
93	9685	9689	9694	9699	9703	9708	9713	9717	9722	9727	0 1 1	2 2 3	3 4 4
94	9731	9736	9741	9745	9750	9754	9759	9763	9768	9773	0 1 1	2 2 3	3 4 4
95	9777	9782	9786	9791	9795	9800	9805	9809	9814	9818	0 1 1	2 2 3	3 4 4
96	9823	9827	9832	9836	9841	9845	9850	9854	9859	9863	0 1 1	2 2 3	3 4 4
97	9868	9872	9877	9881	9886	9890	9894	9899	9903	9908	0 1 1	2 2 3	3 4 4
98	9912	9917	9921	9926	9930	9934	9939	9943	9948	9952	0 1 1	2 2 3	3 4 4
99	9956	9961	9965	9969	9974	9978	9983	9987	9991	9996	0 1 1	2 2 3	3 3 4

	0'	6'	12'	18'	24'	30'	36'	42'	48'	54'	1	2	3	4	5
0°	0000	0017	0035	0052	0070	0087	0105	0122	0140	0157	3	6	9	12	15
1	0175	0192	0209	0227	0244	0262	0279	0297	0314	0332	3	6	9	12	15
2	0349	0366	0384	0401	0419	0436	0454	0471	0488	0506	3	6	9	12	15
3	0523	0541	0558	0576	0593	0610	0628	0645	0663	0680	3	6	9	12	15
4	0698	0715	0732	0750	0767	0785	0802	0819	0837	0854	3	6	9	12	15
5	0872	0889	0906	0924	0941	0958	0976	0993	1011	1028	3	6	9	12	14
6	1045	1063	1080	1097	1115	1132	1149	1167	1184	1201	3	6	9	12	14
7	1219	1236	1253	1271	1288	1305	1323	1340	1357	1374	3	6	9	12	14
8	1392	1409	1426	1444	1461	1478	1495	1513	1530	1547	3	6	9	12	14
9	1564	1582	1599	1616	1633	1650	1668	1685	1702	1719	3	6	9	12	14
10	1736	1754	1771	1788	1805	1822	1840	1857	1874	1891	3	6	9	12	14
11	1908	1925	1942	1959	1977	1994	2011	2028	2045	2062	3	6	9	11	14
12	2079	2096	2113	2130	2147	2164	2181	2198	2215	2232	3	6	9	11	14
13	2250	2267	2284	2300	2317	2334	2351	2368	2385	2402	3	6	8	11	14
14	2419	2436	2453	2470	2487	2504	2521	2538	2554	2571	3	6	8	11	14
15	2588	2605	2622	2639	2656	2672	2689	2706	2723	2740	3	6	8	11	14
16	2756	2773	2790	2807	2823	2840	2857	2874	2890	2907	3	6	8	11	14
17	2924	2940	2957	2974	2990	3007	3024	3040	3057	3074	3	6	8	11	14
18	3090	3107	3123	3140	3156	3173	3190	3206	3223	3239	3	6	8	11	14
19	3256	3272	3289	3305	3322	3338	3355	3371	3387	3404	3	5	8	11	14
20	3420	3437	3453	3469	3486	3502	3518	3535	3551	3567	3	5	8	11	14
21	3584	3600	3616	3633	3649	3665	3681	3697	3714	3730	3	5	8	11	14
22	3746	3762	3778	3795	3811	3827	3843	3859	3875	3891	3	5	8	11	14
23	3907	3923	3939	3955	3971	3987	4003	4019	4035	4051	3	5	8	11	14
24	4067	4083	4099	4115	4131	4147	4163	4179	4195	4210	3	5	8	11	13
25	4226	4242	4258	4274	4289	4305	4321	4337	4352	4368	3	5	8	11	13
26	4384	4399	4415	4431	4446	4462	4478	4493	4509	4524	3	5	8	10	13
27	4540	4555	4571	4586	4602	4617	4633	4648	4664	4679	3	5	8	10	13
28	4695	4710	4726	4741	4756	4772	4787	4802	4818	4833	3	5	8	10	13
29	4848	4863	4879	4894	4909	4924	4939	4955	4970	4985	3	5	8	10	13
30	5000	5015	5030	5045	5060	5075	5090	5105	5120	5135	3	5	8	10	13
31	5150	5165	5180	5195	5210	5225	5240	5255	5270	5284	2	5	7	10	12
32	5299	5314	5329	5344	5358	5373	5388	5402	5417	5432	2	5	7	10	12
33	5446	5461	5476	5490	5505	5519	5534	5548	5563	5577	2	5	7	10	12
34	5592	5606	5621	5635	5650	5664	5678	5693	5707	5721	2	5	7	10	12
35	5736	5750	5764	5779	5793	5807	5821	5835	5850	5864	2	5	7	10	12
36	5878	5892	5906	5920	5934	5948	5962	5976	5990	6004	2	5	7	9	12
37	6018	6032	6046	6060	6074	6088	6101	6115	6129	6143	2	5	7	9	12
38	6157	6170	6184	6198	6211	6225	6239	6252	6266	6280	2	5	7	9	11
39	6293	6307	6320	6334	6347	6361	6374	6388	6401	6414	2	4	7	9	11
40	6428	6441	6455	6468	6481	6494	6508	6521	6534	6547	2	4	7	9	11
41	6561	6574	6587	6600	6613	6626	6639	6652	6665	6678	2	4	7	9	11
42	6691	6704	6717	6730	6743	6756	6769	6782	6794	6807	2	4	6	9	11
43	6820	6833	6845	6858	6871	6884	6896	6909	6921	6934	2	4	6	8	11
44	6947	6959	6972	6984	6997	7009	7022	7034	7046	7059	2	4	6	8	10

	0'	6'	12'	18'	24'	30'	36'	42'	48'	54'	1	2	3	4	5
45°	7071	7083	7096	7108	7120	7133	7145	7157	7169	7181	2	4	6	8	10
46	7193	7206	7218	7230	7242	7254	7266	7278	7290	7302	2	4	6	8	10
47	7314	7325	7337	7349	7361	7373	7385	7396	7408	7420	2	4	6	8	10
48	7431	7443	7455	7466	7478	7490	7501	7513	7524	7536	2	4	6	8	10
49	7547	7558	7570	7581	7593	7604	7615	7627	7638	7649	2	4	6	8	9
50	7660	7672	7683	7694	7705	7716	7727	7738	7749	7760	2	4	6	7	9
51	7771	7782	7793	7804	7815	7826	7837	7848	7859	7869	2	4	5	7	9
52	7880	7891	7902	7912	7923	7934	7944	7955	7965	7976	2	4	5	7	9
53	7986	7997	8007	8018	8028	8039	8049	8059	8070	8080	2	3	5	7	9
54	8090	8100	8111	8121	8131	8141	8151	8161	8171	8181	2	3	5	7	8
55	8192	8202	8211	8221	8231	8241	8251	8261	8271	8281	2	3	5	7	8
56	8290	8300	8310	8320	8329	8339	8348	8358	8368	8377	2	3	5	6	8
57	8387	8396	8406	8415	8425	8434	8443	8453	8462	8471	2	3	5	6	8
58	8480	8490	8499	8508	8517	8526	8536	8545	8554	8563	2	3	5	6	8
59	8572	8581	8590	8599	8607	8616	8625	8634	8643	8652	1	3	4	6	7
60	8660	8669	8678	8686	8695	8704	8712	8721	8729	8738	1	3	4	6	7
61	8746	8755	8763	8771	8780	8788	8796	8805	8813	8821	1	3	4	6	7
62	8829	8838	8846	8854	8862	8870	8878	8886	8894	8902	1	3	4	5	7
63	8910	8918	8926	8934	8942	8949	8957	8965	8973	8980	1	3	4	5	6
64	8988	8996	9003	9011	9018	9026	9033	9041	9048	9056	1	3	4	5	6
65	9063	9070	9078	9085	9092	9100	9107	9114	9121	9128	1	2	4	5	6
66	9135	9143	9150	9157	9164	9171	9178	9184	9191	9198	1	2	3	5	6
67	9205	9212	9219	9225	9232	9239	9245	9252	9259	9265	1	2	3	4	6
68	9272	9278	9285	9291	9298	9304	9311	9317	9323	9330	1	2	3	4	5
69	9336	9342	9348	9354	9361	9367	9373	9379	9385	9391	1	2	3	4	5
70	9397	9403	9409	9415	9421	9426	9432	9438	9444	9449	1	2	3	4	5
71	9455	9461	9466	9472	9478	9483	9489	9494	9500	9505	1	2	3	4	5
72	9511	9516	9521	9527	9532	9537	9542	9548	9553	9558	1	2	3	4	4
73	9563	9568	9573	9578	9583	9588	9593	9598	9603	9608	1	2	2	3	4
74	9613	9617	9622	9627	9632	9636	9641	9646	9650	9655	1	2	2	3	4
75	9659	9664	9668	9673	9677	9681	9686	9690	9694	9699	1	1	2	3	4
76	9703	9707	9711	9715	9720	9724	9728	9732	9736	9740	1	1	2	3	3
77	9744	9748	9751	9755	9759	9763	9767	9770	9774	9778	1	1	2	3	3
78	9781	9785	9789	9792	9796	9799	9803	9806	9810	9813	1	1	2	2	3
79	9816	9820	9823	9826	9829	9833	9836	9839	9842	9845	1	1	2	2	3
80	9848	9851	9854	9857	9860	9863	9866	9869	9871	9874	0	1	1	2	2
81	9877	9880	9882	9885	9888	9890	9893	9895	9898	9900	0	1	1	2	2
82	9903	9905	9907	9910	9912	9914	9917	9919	9921	9923	0	1	1	2	2
83	9925	9928	9930	9932	9934	9936	9938	9940	9942	9943	0	1	1	1	2
84	9945	9947	9949	9951	9952	9954	9956	9957	9959	9960	0	1	1	1	1
85	9962	9963	9965	9966	9968	9969	9971	9972	9973	9974	0	0	1	1	1
86	9976	9977	9978	9979	9980	9981	9982	9983	9984	9985	0	0	1	1	1
87	9986	9987	9988	9989	9990	9990	9991	9992	9993	9993	0	0	0	1	1
88	9994	9995	9995	9996	9996	9997	9997	9997	9998	9998	0	0	0	0	0
89	9998	9999	9999	9999	9999	1.000 nearly	1.000 nearly	1.000 nearly	1.000 nearly	1.000 nearly	0	0	0	0	0

	0′	6′	12′	18′	24′	30′	36′	42′	48′	54′	1	2	3	4	5
0°	1.000	1.000 nearly	1.000 nearly	1.000 nearly	1.000 nearly	9999	9999	9999	9999	9999	0	0	0	0	0
1	9998	9998	9998	9997	9997	9997	9996	9996	9995	9995	0	0	0	0	0
2	9994	9993	9993	9992	9991	9990	9990	9989	9988	9987	0	0	0	1	1
3	9986	9985	9984	9983	9982	9981	9980	9979	9978	9977	0	0	1	1	1
4	9976	9974	9973	9972	9971	9969	9968	9966	9965	9963	0	0	1	1	1
5	9962	9960	9959	9957	9956	9954	9952	9951	9949	9947	0	1	1	1	2
6	9945	9943	9942	9940	9938	9936	9934	9932	9930	9928	0	1	1	1	2
7	9925	9923	9921	9919	9917	9914	9912	9910	9907	9905	0	1	1	2	2
8	9903	9900	9898	9895	9893	9890	9888	9885	9882	9880	0	1	1	2	2
9	9877	9874	9871	9869	9866	9863	9860	9857	9854	9851	0	1	1	2	2
10	9848	9845	9842	9839	9836	9833	9829	9826	9823	9820	1	1	2	2	3
11	9816	9813	9810	9806	9803	9799	9796	9792	9789	9785	1	1	2	2	3
12	9781	9778	9774	9770	9767	9763	9759	9755	9751	9748	1	1	2	3	3
13	9744	9740	9736	9732	9728	9724	9720	9715	9711	9707	1	1	2	3	3
14	9703	9699	9694	9690	9686	9681	9677	9673	9668	9664	1	1	2	3	4
15	9659	9655	9650	9646	9641	9636	9632	9627	9622	9617	1	2	2	3	4
16	9613	9608	9603	9598	9593	9588	9583	9578	9573	9568	1	2	2	3	4
17	9563	9558	9553	9548	9542	9537	9532	9527	9521	9516	1	2	3	4	4
18	9511	9505	9500	9494	9489	9483	9478	9472	9466	9461	1	2	3	4	5
19	9455	9449	9444	9438	9432	9426	9421	9415	9409	9403	1	2	3	4	5
20	9397	9391	9385	9379	9373	9367	9361	9354	9348	9342	1	2	3	4	5
21	9336	9330	9323	9317	9311	9304	9298	9291	9285	9278	1	2	3	4	5
22	9272	9265	9259	9252	9245	9239	9232	9225	9219	9212	1	2	3	4	6
23	9205	9198	9191	9184	9178	9171	9164	9157	9150	9143	1	2	3	5	6
24	9135	9128	9121	9114	9107	9100	9092	9085	9078	9070	1	2	4	5	6
25	9063	9056	9048	9041	9033	9026	9018	9011	9003	8996	1	3	4	5	6
26	8988	8980	8973	8965	8957	8949	8942	8934	8926	8918	1	3	4	5	6
27	8910	8902	8894	8886	8878	8870	8862	8854	8846	8838	1	3	4	5	7
28	8829	8821	8813	8805	8796	8788	8780	8771	8763	8755	1	3	4	6	7
29	8746	8738	8729	8721	8712	8704	8695	8686	8678	8669	1	3	4	6	7
30	8660	8652	8643	8634	8625	8616	8607	8599	8590	8581	1	3	4	6	7
31	8572	8563	8554	8545	8536	8526	8517	8508	8499	8490	2	3	5	6	8
32	8480	8471	8462	8453	8443	8434	8425	8415	8406	8396	2	3	5	6	8
33	8387	8377	8368	8358	8348	8339	8329	8320	8310	8300	2	3	5	6	8
34	8290	8281	8271	8261	8251	8241	8231	8221	8211	8202	2	3	5	7	8
35	8192	8181	8171	8161	8151	8141	8131	8121	8111	8100	2	3	5	7	8
36	8090	8080	8070	8059	8049	8039	8028	8018	8007	7997	2	3	5	7	9
37	7986	7976	7965	7955	7944	7934	7923	7912	7902	7891	2	4	5	7	9
38	7880	7869	7859	7848	7837	7826	7815	7804	7793	7782	2	4	5	7	9
39	7771	7760	7749	7738	7727	7716	7705	7694	7683	7672	2	4	6	7	9
40	7660	7649	7638	7627	7615	7604	7593	7581	7570	7559	2	4	6	8	9
41	7547	7536	7524	7513	7501	7490	7478	7466	7455	7443	2	4	6	8	10
42	7431	7420	7408	7396	7385	7373	7361	7349	7337	7325	2	4	6	8	10
43	7314	7302	7290	7278	7266	7254	7242	7230	7218	7206	2	4	6	8	10
44	7193	7181	7169	7157	7145	7133	7120	7108	7096	7083	2	4	6	8	10

N.B.—Numbers in difference columns to be subtracted, not added.

	0'	6'	12'	18'	24'	30'	36'	42'	48'	54'	1	2	3	4	5
45°	7071	7059	7046	7034	7022	7009	6997	6984	6972	6959	2	4	6	8	10
46	6947	6934	6921	6909	6896	6884	6871	6858	6845	6833	2	4	6	8	11
47	6820	6807	6794	6782	6769	6756	6743	6730	6717	6704	2	4	6	9	11
48	6691	6678	6665	6652	6639	6626	6613	6600	6587	6574	2	4	7	9	11
49	6561	6547	6534	6521	6508	6494	6481	6468	6455	6441	2	4	7	9	11
50	6428	6414	6401	6388	6374	6361	6347	6334	6320	6307	2	4	7	9	11
51	6293	6280	6266	6252	6239	6225	6211	6198	6184	6170	2	5	7	9	11
52	6157	6143	6129	6115	6101	6088	6074	6060	6046	6032	2	5	7	9	12
53	6018	6004	5990	5976	5962	5948	5934	5920	5906	5892	2	5	7	9	12
54	5878	5864	5850	5835	5821	5807	5793	5779	5764	5750	2	5	7	9	12
55	5736	5721	5707	5693	5678	5664	5650	5635	5621	5606	2	5	7	10	12
56	5592	5577	5563	5548	5534	5519	5505	5490	5476	5461	2	5	7	10	12
57	5446	5432	5417	5402	5388	5373	5358	5344	5329	5314	2	5	7	10	12
58	5299	5284	5270	5255	5240	5225	5210	5195	5180	5165	2	5	7	10	12
59	5150	5135	5120	5105	5090	5075	5060	5045	5030	5015	3	5	8	10	13
60	5000	4985	4970	4955	4939	4924	4909	4894	4879	4863	3	5	8	10	13
61	4848	4833	4818	4802	4787	4772	4756	4741	4726	4710	3	5	8	10	13
62	4695	4679	4664	4648	4633	4617	4602	4586	4571	4555	3	5	8	10	13
63	4540	4524	4509	4493	4478	4462	4446	4431	4415	4399	3	5	8	10	13
64	4384	4368	4352	4337	4321	4305	4289	4274	4258	4242	3	5	8	11	13
65	4226	4210	4195	4179	4163	4147	4131	4115	4099	4083	3	5	8	11	13
66	4067	4051	4035	4019	4003	3987	3971	3955	3939	3923	3	5	8	11	14
67	3907	3891	3875	3859	3843	3827	3811	3795	3778	3762	3	5	8	11	14
68	3746	3730	3714	3697	3681	3665	3649	3633	3616	3600	3	5	8	11	14
69	3584	3567	3551	3535	3518	3502	3486	3469	3453	3437	3	5	8	11	14
70	3420	3404	3387	3371	3355	3338	3322	3305	3289	3272	3	5	8	11	14
71	3256	3239	3223	3206	3190	3173	3156	3140	3123	3107	3	6	8	11	14
72	3090	3074	3057	3040	3024	3007	2990	2974	2957	2940	3	6	8	11	14
73	2924	2907	2890	2874	2857	2840	2823	2807	2790	2773	3	6	8	11	14
74	2756	2740	2723	2706	2689	2672	2656	2639	2622	2605	3	6	8	11	14
75	2588	2571	2554	2538	2521	2504	2487	2470	2453	2436	3	6	8	11	14
76	2419	2402	2385	2368	2351	2334	2317	2300	2284	2267	3	6	8	11	14
77	2250	2233	2215	2198	2181	2164	2147	2130	2113	2096	3	6	9	11	14
78	2079	2062	2045	2028	2011	1994	1977	1959	1942	1925	3	6	9	11	14
79	1908	1891	1874	1857	1840	1822	1805	1788	1771	1754	3	6	9	12	14
80	1736	1719	1702	1685	1668	1650	1633	1616	1599	1582	3	6	9	12	14
81	1564	1547	1530	1513	1495	1478	1461	1444	1426	1409	3	6	9	12	14
82	1392	1374	1357	1340	1323	1305	1288	1271	1253	1236	3	6	9	12	14
83	1219	1201	1184	1167	1149	1132	1115	1097	1080	1063	3	6	9	12	14
84	1045	1028	1011	0993	0976	0958	0941	0924	0906	0889	3	6	9	12	14
85	0872	0854	0837	0819	0802	0785	0767	0750	0732	0715	3	6	9	12	15
86	0698	0680	0663	0645	0628	0610	0593	0576	0558	0541	3	6	9	12	15
87	0523	0506	0488	0471	0454	0436	0419	0401	0384	0366	3	6	9	12	15
88	0349	0332	0314	0297	0279	0262	0244	0227	0209	0192	3	6	9	12	15
89	0175	0157	0140	0122	0105	0087	0070	0052	0035	0017	3	6	9	12	15

N.B.—Numbers in difference columns to be subtracted, not added.

	0'	6'	12'	18'	24'	30'	36'	42'	48'	54'	1	2	3	4	5
0°	.0000	0017	0035	0052	0070	0087	0105	0122	0140	0157	3	6	9	12	14
1	.0175	0192	0209	0227	0244	0262	0279	0297	0314	0332	3	6	9	12	15
2	.0349	0367	0384	0402	0419	0437	0454	0472	0489	0507	3	6	9	12	15
3	.0524	0542	0559	0577	0594	0612	0629	0647	0664	0682	3	6	9	12	15
4	.0699	0717	0734	0752	0769	0787	0805	0822	0840	0857	3	6	9	12	15
5	.0875	0892	0910	0928	0945	0963	0981	0998	1016	1033	3	6	9	12	15
6	.1051	1069	1086	1104	1122	1139	1157	1175	1192	1210	3	6	9	12	15
7	.1228	1246	1263	1281	1299	1317	1334	1352	1370	1388	3	6	9	12	15
8	.1405	1423	1441	1459	1477	1495	1512	1530	1548	1566	3	6	9	12	15
9	.1584	1602	1620	1638	1655	1673	1691	1709	1727	1745	3	6	9	12	15
10	.1763	1781	1799	1817	1835	1853	1871	1890	1908	1926	3	6	9	12	15
11	.1944	1962	1980	1998	2016	2035	2053	2071	2089	2107	3	6	9	12	15
12	.2126	2144	2162	2180	2199	2217	2235	2254	2272	2290	3	6	9	12	15
13	.2309	2327	2345	2364	2382	2401	2419	2438	2456	2475	3	6	9	12	15
14	.2493	2512	2530	2549	2568	2586	2605	2623	2642	2661	3	6	9	12	16
15	.2679	2698	2717	2736	2754	2773	2792	2811	2830	2849	3	6	9	13	16
16	.2867	2886	2905	2924	2943	2962	2981	3000	3019	3038	3	6	9	13	16
17	.3057	3076	3096	3115	3134	3153	3172	3191	3211	3230	3	6	10	13	16
18	.3249	3269	3288	3307	3327	3346	3365	3385	3404	3424	3	6	10	13	16
19	.3443	3463	3482	3502	3522	3541	3561	3581	3600	3620	3	6	10	13	17
20	.3640	3659	3679	3699	3719	3739	3759	3779	3799	3819	3	7	10	13	17
21	.3839	3859	3879	3899	3919	3939	3959	3978	4000	4020	3	7	10	13	17
22	.4040	4061	4081	4101	4122	4142	4163	4183	4204	4224	3	7	10	14	17
23	.4245	4265	4286	4307	4327	4348	4369	4390	4411	4431	3	7	10	14	17
24	.4452	4473	4494	4515	4536	4557	4578	4599	4621	4642	4	7	10	14	18
25	.4663	4684	4706	4727	4748	4770	4791	4813	4834	4856	4	7	11	14	18
26	.4877	4899	4921	4942	4964	4986	5008	5029	5051	5073	4	7	11	15	18
27	.5095	5117	5139	5161	5184	5206	5228	5250	5272	5295	4	7	11	15	18
28	.5317	5340	5362	5384	5407	5430	5452	5475	5498	5520	4	8	11	15	19
29	.5543	5566	5589	5612	5635	5658	5681	5704	5727	5750	4	8	12	15	19
30	.5774	5797	5820	5844	5867	5890	5914	5938	5961	5985	4	8	12	16	20
31	.6009	6032	6056	6080	6104	6128	6152	6176	6200	6224	4	8	12	16	20
32	.6249	6273	6297	6322	6346	6371	6395	6420	6445	6469	4	8	12	16	20
33	.6494	6519	6544	6569	6594	6619	6644	6669	6694	6720	4	8	13	17	21
34	.6745	6771	6796	6822	6847	6873	6899	6924	6950	6976	4	9	13	17	21
35	.7002	7028	7054	7080	7107	7133	7159	7186	7212	7239	4	9	13	18	22
36	.7265	7292	7319	7346	7373	7400	7427	7454	7481	7508	5	9	14	18	23
37	.7536	7563	7590	7618	7646	7673	7701	7729	7757	7785	5	9	14	18	23
38	.7813	7841	7869	7898	7926	7954	7983	8012	8040	8069	5	10	14	19	24
39	.8098	8127	8156	8185	8214	8243	8273	8302	8332	8361	5	10	15	20	24
40	.8391	8421	8451	8481	8511	8541	8571	8601	8632	8662	5	10	15	20	25
41	.8693	8724	8754	8785	8816	8847	8878	8910	8941	8972	5	10	16	21	26
42	.9004	9036	9067	9099	9131	9163	9195	9228	9260	9293	5	11	16	21	27
43	.9325	9358	9391	9424	9457	9490	9523	9556	9590	9623	6	11	17	22	28
44	.9657	9691	9725	9759	9793	9827	9861	9896	9930	9965	6	11	17	23	29

	0'	6'	12'	18'	24'	30'	36'	42'	48'	54'	1	2	3	4	5
45°	1.0000	0035	0070	0105	0141	0176	0212	0247	0283	0319	6	12	18	24	30
46	1.0355	0392	0428	0464	0501	0538	0575	0612	0649	0686	6	12	18	25	31
47	1.0724	0761	0799	0837	0875	0913	0951	0990	1028	1067	6	13	19	25	32
48	1.1106	1145	1184	1224	1263	1303	1343	1383	1423	1463	7	13	20	26	33
49	1.1504	1544	1585	1626	1667	1708	1750	1792	1833	1875	7	14	21	28	34
50	1.1918	1960	2002	2045	2088	2131	2174	2218	2261	2305	7	14	22	29	36
51	1.2349	2393	2437	2482	2527	2572	2617	2662	2708	2753	8	15	23	30	38
52	1.2799	2846	2892	2938	2985	3032	3079	3127	3175	3222	8	16	23	31	39
53	1.3270	3319	3367	3416	3465	3514	3564	3613	3663	3713	8	16	25	33	41
54	1.3764	3814	3865	3916	3968	4019	4071	4124	4176	4229	9	17	26	34	43
55	1.4281	4335	4388	4442	4496	4550	4605	4659	4715	4770	9	18	27	36	45
56	1.4826	4882	4938	4994	5051	5108	5166	5224	5282	5340	10	19	29	38	48
57	1.5399	5458	5517	5577	5637	5697	5757	5818	5880	5941	10	20	30	40	50
58	1.6003	6066	6128	6191	6255	6319	6383	6447	6512	6577	11	21	32	43	53
59	1.6643	6709	6775	6842	6909	6977	7045	7113	7182	7251	11	23	34	45	56
60	1.7321	7391	7461	7532	7603	7675	7747	7820	7893	7966	12	24	36	48	60
61	1.8040	8115	8190	8265	8341	8418	8495	8572	8650	8728	13	26	38	51	64
62	1.8807	8887	8967	9047	9128	9210	9292	9375	9458	9542	14	27	41	55	68
63	1.9626	9711	9797	9883	9970	0057	0145	0233	0323	0413	15	29	44	58	73
64	2.0503	0594	0686	0778	0872	0965	1060	1155	1251	1348	16	31	47	63	78
65	2.1445	1543	1642	1742	1842	1943	2045	2148	2251	2355	17	34	51	68	85
66	2.2460	2566	2673	2781	2889	2998	3109	3220	3332	3445	18	37	55	74	92
67	2.3559	3673	3789	3906	4023	4142	4262	4383	4504	4627	20	40	60	79	99
68	2.4751	4876	5002	5129	5257	5386	5517	5649	5782	5916	22	43	65	87	108
69	2.6051	6187	6325	6464	6605	6746	6889	7034	7179	7326	24	47	71	95	118
70	2.7475	7625	7776	7929	8083	8239	8397	8556	8716	8878	26	52	78	104	130
71	2.9042	9208	9375	9544	9714	9887	0061	0237	0415	0595	29	58	87	115	144
72	3.0777	0961	1146	1334	1524	1716	1910	2106	2305	2506	32	64	96	129	161
73	3.2709	2914	3122	3332	3544	3759	3977	4197	4420	4646	36	72	108	144	180
74	3.4874	5105	5339	5576	5816	6059	6305	6554	6806	7062	41	82	122	162	203
75	3.7321	7583	7848	8118	8391	8667	8947	9232	9520	9812	46	94	139	186	232
76	4.0108	0408	0713	1022	1335	1653	1976	2303	2635	2972	53	107	160	214	267
77	4.3315	3662	4015	4374	4737	5107	5483	5864	6252	6646	62	124	186	248	310
78	4.7046	7453	7867	8288	8716	9152	9594	0045	0504	0970	73	146	219	292	365
79	5.1446	1929	2422	2924	3435	3955	4486	5026	5578	6140	87	175	262	350	437
80	5.6713	7297	7894	8502	9124	9758	0405	1066	1742	2432					
81	6.3138	3859	4596	5350	6122	6912	7920	8548	9395	0264					
82	7.1154	2066	3002	3962	4947	5958	6996	8062	9158	0285					
83	8.1443	2636	3863	5126	6427	7769	9152	0579	2052	3572					
84	9.5144	9.677	9.845	10.02	10.20	10.39	10.58	10.78	10.99	11.20					
85	11.43	11.66	11.91	12.16	12.43	12.71	13.00	13.30	13.62	13.95					
86	14.30	14.67	15.06	15.46	15.89	16.35	16.83	17.34	17.89	18.46					
87	19.08	19.74	20.45	21.20	22.02	22.90	23.86	24.90	26.03	27.27					
88	28.64	30.14	31.82	33.69	35.80	38.19	40.92	44.07	47.74	52.08					
89	57.29	63.66	71.62	81.85	95.49	114.6	143.2	191.0	286.5	573.0					

Difference - columns cease to be useful, owing to the rapidity with which the value of the tangent changes.

°	0'	6'	12'	18'	24'	30'	36'	42'	48'	54'	1	2	3	4	5
0	−∞	7.242	5429	7̄190	8439	9408	0̄200	0̄870	1̄450	1̄961					
1	8.2419	2832	3210	3558	3880	4179	4459	4723	4971	5206					
2	8.5428	5640	5842	6035	6220	6397	6567	6731	6889	7041		Difference useless			
3	8.7188	7330	7468	7602	7731	7857	7979	8098	8213	8326		due to rapidity of			
4	8.8436	8543	8647	8749	8849	8946	9042	9135	9226	9315		change in log sine.			
5	8.9403	9489	9573	9655	9736	9816	9894	9970	0̄046	0̄120					
6	9.0192	0264	0334	0403	0472	0539	0605	0670	0734	0797					
7	9.0859	0920	0981	1040	1099	1157	1214	1271	1326	1381	9	19	29	39	48
8	9.1436	1489	1542	1594	1646	1697	1747	1797	1847	1895	9	17	24	33	41
9	9.1943	1991	2038	2085	2131	2176	2221	2266	2310	2353	8	15	23	29	36
10	9.2397	2439	2482	2524	2565	2606	2647	2687	2727	2767	7	14	20	27	34
11	9.2806	2845	2883	2921	2959	2997	3034	3070	3107	3143	6	12	19	25	31
12	9.3179	3214	3250	3284	3319	3353	3387	3421	3455	3488	6	11	17	23	28
13	9.3521	3554	3586	3618	3650	3682	3713	3745	3775	3806	5	10	16	21	27
14	9.3837	3867	3897	3927	3957	3986	4015	4044	4073	4102	5	10	15	20	25
15	9.4130	4158	4186	4214	4242	4269	4296	4323	4350	4377	5	9	14	18	23
16	9.4403	4430	4456	4482	4508	4533	4559	4584	4609	4634	4	9	13	17	22
17	9.4659	4684	4709	4733	4757	4781	4805	4829	4853	4876	4	8	12	16	19
18	9.4900	4923	4946	4969	4992	5015	5037	5060	5082	5104	4	8	11	15	18
19	9.5126	5148	5170	5192	5213	5235	5256	5278	5299	5320	4	7	11	14	18
20	9.5341	5361	5382	5402	5423	5443	5463	5484	5504	5523	3	7	10	13	16
21	9.5543	5563	5583	5602	5621	5641	5660	5679	5698	5717	3	7	10	13	16
22	9.5736	5754	5773	5792	5810	5828	5847	5865	5883	5901	3	6	9	12	15
23	9.5919	5937	5954	5972	5990	6007	6024	6042	6059	6076	3	6	9	12	14
24	9.6093	6110	6127	6144	6161	6177	6194	6210	6227	6243	3	6	8	11	13
25	9.6259	6276	6292	6308	6324	6340	6356	6371	6387	6403	3	6	8	11	13
26	9.6418	6434	6449	6465	6480	6495	6510	6526	6541	6556	3	5	8	10	13
27	9.6570	6585	6600	6615	6629	6644	6659	6673	6687	6702	3	5	8	10	12
28	9.6716	6730	6744	6759	6773	6787	6801	6814	6828	6842	2	5	7	10	12
29	9.6856	6869	6883	6896	6910	6923	6937	6950	6963	6977	2	4	7	9	11
30	9.6990	7003	7016	7029	7042	7055	7068	7080	7093	7106	2	4	7	9	11
31	9.7118	7131	7143	7156	7168	7181	7193	7205	7218	7230	2	4	6	8	10
32	9.7242	7254	7266	7278	7290	7302	7314	7326	7338	7349	2	4	6	8	10
33	9.7361	7373	7384	7396	7407	7419	7430	7442	7453	7464	2	4	6	8	9
34	9.7476	7487	7498	7509	7520	7531	7542	7553	7564	7575	2	4	6	7	9
35	9.7586	7597	7607	7618	7629	7640	7650	7661	7671	7682	2	4	5	7	9
36	9.7692	7703	7713	7723	7734	7744	7754	7764	7774	7785	2	4	5	7	9
37	9.7795	7805	7815	7825	7835	7844	7854	7864	7874	7884	2	3	5	7	8
38	9.7893	7903	7913	7922	7932	7941	7951	7960	7970	7979	2	3	5	6	8
39	9.7989	7998	8007	8017	8026	8035	8044	8053	8063	8072	2	3	5	6	8
40	9.8081	8090	8099	8108	8117	8125	8134	8143	8152	8161	2	3	5	6	8
41	9.8169	8178	8187	8195	8204	8213	8221	8230	8238	8247	2	3	5	6	8
42	9.8255	8264	8272	8280	8289	8297	8305	8313	8322	8330	2	3	4	5	7
43	9.8338	8346	8354	8362	8370	8378	8386	8394	8402	8410	1	3	4	5	7
44	9.8418	8426	8433	8441	8449	8457	8464	8472	8480	8487	1	3	4	5	6

After each function as taken from the table is to be written −10.

°	0′	6′	12′	18′	24′	30′	36′	42′	48′	54′	1	2	3	4	5
45	9.8495	8502	8510	8517	8525	8532	8540	8547	8555	8562	1	2	4	5	6
46	9.8569	8577	8584	8591	8598	8606	8613	8620	8627	8634	1	2	4	5	6
47	9.8641	8648	8655	8662	8669	8676	8683	8690	8697	8704	1	2	4	5	6
48	9.8711	8718	8724	8731	8738	8745	8751	8758	8765	8771	1	2	3	4	5
49	9.8778	8784	8791	8797	8804	8810	8817	8823	8830	8836	1	2	3	4	5
50	9.8843	8849	8855	8862	8868	8874	8880	8887	8893	8899	1	2	3	4	5
51	9.8905	8911	8917	8923	8929	8935	8941	8947	8953	8959	1	2	3	4	5
52	9.8965	8971	8977	8983	8989	8995	9000	9006	9012	9018	1	2	3	4	5
53	9.9023	9029	9035	9041	9046	9052	9057	9063	9069	9074	1	2	3	4	5
54	9.9080	9085	9091	9096	9101	9107	9112	9118	9123	9128	1	2	3	3	4
55	9.9134	9139	9144	9149	9155	9160	9165	9170	9175	9181	1	2	3	3	4
56	9.9186	9191	9196	9201	9206	9211	9216	9221	9226	9231	1	2	3	3	4
57	9.9236	9241	9246	9251	9255	9260	9265	9270	9275	9279	1	2	3	3	4
58	9.9284	9289	9294	9298	9303	9308	9312	9317	9322	9326	1	2	2	3	4
59	9.9331	9335	9340	9344	9349	9353	9358	9362	9367	9371	1	2	2	3	4
60	9.9375	9380	9384	9388	9393	9397	9401	9406	9410	9414	1	2	2	3	4
61	9.9418	9422	9427	9431	9435	9439	9443	9447	9451	9455	1	2	2	3	4
62	9.9459	9463	9467	9471	9475	9479	9483	9487	9491	9495	1	2	2	3	4
63	9.9499	9503	9506	9510	9514	9518	9522	9525	9529	9533	1	2	2	3	4
64	9.9537	9540	9544	9548	9551	9555	9558	9562	9566	9569	1	1	2	2	3
65	9.9573	9576	9580	9583	9587	9590	9594	9597	9601	9604	1	1	2	2	3
66	9.9607	9611	9614	9617	9621	9624	9627	9631	9634	9637	1	1	2	2	3
67	9.9640	9643	9647	9650	9653	9656	9659	9662	9666	9669	1	1	2	2	3
68	9.9672	9675	9678	9681	9684	9687	9690	9693	9696	9699	1	1	2	2	3
69	9.9702	9704	9707	9710	9713	9716	9719	9722	9724	9727	1	1	2	2	3
70	9.9730	9733	9735	9738	9741	9743	9746	9749	9751	9754	1	1	2	2	3
71	9.9757	9759	9762	9764	9767	9770	9772	9775	9777	9780	1	1	2	2	3
72	9.9782	9785	9787	9789	9792	9794	9797	9799	9801	9804	1	1	2	2	3
73	9.9806	9808	9811	9813	9815	9817	9820	9822	9824	9826	0	1	1	1	2
74	9.9828	9831	9833	9835	9837	9839	9841	9843	9845	9847	0	1	1	1	2
75	9.9849	9851	9853	9855	9857	9859	9861	9863	9865	9867	0	1	1	1	2
76	9.9869	9871	9873	9875	9876	9878	9880	9882	9884	9885	0	1	1	1	2
77	9.9887	9889	9891	9892	9894	9896	9897	9899	9901	9902	0	1	1	1	2
78	9.9904	9906	9907	9909	9910	9912	9913	9915	9916	9918	0	1	1	1	2
79	9.9919	9921	9922	9924	9925	9927	9928	9929	9931	9932	0	1	1	1	2
80	9.9934	9935	9936	9937	9939	9940	9941	9943	9944	9945	0	0	1	1	1
81	9.9946	9947	9949	9950	9951	9952	9953	9954	9955	9956	0	0	1	1	1
82	9.9958	9959	9960	9961	9962	9963	9964	9965	9966	9967	0	0	1	1	1
83	9.9968	9968	9969	9970	9971	9972	9973	9974	9975	9975	0	0	0	1	1
84	9.9976	9977	9978	9978	9979	9980	9981	9981	9982	9983	0	0	0	1	1
85	9.9983	9984	9985	9985	9986	9987	9987	9988	9988	9989	0	0	0	1	1
86	9.9989	9990	9990	9991	9991	9992	9992	9993	9993	9994	0	0	0	0	1
87	9.9994	9994	9995	9995	9996	9996	9996	9996	9997	9997	0	0	0	0	0
88	9.9997	9998	9998	9998	9998	9999	9999	9999	9999	9999	0	0	0	0	0
89	10.000	0000	0000	0000	0000	0000	0000	0000	0000	0000	0	0	0	0	0

After each function as taken from the table is to be written − 10.

°	0′	6′	12′	18′	24′	30′	36′	42′	48′	54′	1	2	3	4	5
0	10.000	0000	0000	0000	0000	0000	0000	0000	0000	9999	0	0	0	0	0
1	9.9999	9999	9999	9999	9999	9999	9998	9998	9998	9998	0	0	0	0	0
2	9.9997	9997	9997	9996	9996	9996	9996	9995	9995	9994	0	0	0	0	0
3	9.9994	9994	9993	9993	9992	9992	9991	9991	9990	9990	0	0	0	0	0
4	9.9989	9989	9988	9988	9987	9987	9986	9985	9985	9984	0	0	0	0	1
5	9.9983	9983	9982	9981	9981	9980	9979	9978	9978	9877	0	0	0	1	1
6	9.9976	9975	9975	9974	9973	9972	9971	9970	9970	9968	0	0	0	1	1
7	9.9968	9967	9966	9965	9964	9963	9962	9961	9960	9959	0	0	0	1	1
8	9.9958	9956	9955	9954	9953	9952	9951	9950	9949	9947	0	0	1	1	1
9	9.9946	9945	9944	9943	9941	9940	9939	9937	9936	9935	0	0	1	1	1
10	9.9934	9932	9931	9929	9928	9927	9925	9924	9922	9921	0	0	1	1	1
11	9.9919	9918	9916	9915	9913	9912	9910	9909	9907	9906	0	0	1	1	1
12	9.9904	9902	9901	9899	9897	9896	9894	9892	9891	9889	0	1	1	1	2
13	9.9887	9885	9884	9882	9880	9878	9876	9875	9873	9871	0	1	1	1	2
14	9.9869	9867	9865	9863	9861	9859	9857	9855	9853	9851	0	1	1	1	2
15	9.9849	9847	9845	9843	9841	9839	9837	9835	9833	9831	0	1	1	1	2
16	9.9828	9826	9824	9822	9820	9817	9815	9813	9811	9808	0	1	1	1	2
17	9.9806	9804	9801	9799	9797	9794	9792	9789	9787	9784	0	1	1	1	2
18	9.9782	9780	9777	9775	9772	9770	9767	9764	9762	9759	0	1	1	1	2
19	9.9757	9754	9751	9749	9746	9743	9741	9738	9735	9733	1	1	2	2	3
20	9.9730	9727	9724	9722	9719	9716	9713	9710	9707	9704	1	1	2	2	3
21	9.9702	9699	9696	9693	9690	9687	9684	9681	9678	9675	1	1	2	2	3
22	9.9672	9669	9666	9662	9659	9656	9653	9650	9647	9643	1	1	2	2	3
23	9.9640	9637	9634	9631	9627	9624	9621	9617	9614	9611	1	1	2	2	3
24	9.9607	9604	9601	9597	9594	9590	9587	9583	9580	9576	1	1	2	2	3
25	9.9573	9569	9566	9562	9558	9555	9551	9548	9544	9540	1	1	2	2	3
26	9.9537	9533	9529	9525	9522	9518	9514	9510	9506	9503	1	1	2	2	3
27	9.9499	9495	9491	9487	9483	9479	9475	9471	9467	9463	1	2	2	3	4
28	9.9459	9455	9451	9447	9443	9439	9435	9431	9427	9422	1	2	2	3	4
29	9.9418	9414	9410	9406	9401	9397	9393	9388	9384	9380	1	2	2	3	4
30	9.9375	9371	9367	9362	9358	9353	9349	9344	9340	9335	1	2	2	3	4
31	9.9331	9326	9322	9317	9312	9308	9303	9298	9294	9289	1	2	2	3	4
32	9.9284	9279	9275	9270	9265	9260	9255	9251	9246	9241	1	2	3	3	4
33	9.9236	9231	9226	9221	9216	9211	9206	9201	9196	9191	1	2	3	3	4
34	9.9186	9181	9175	9170	9165	9160	9155	9149	9144	9139	1	2	3	3	4
35	9.9134	9128	9123	9118	9112	9107	9101	9096	9091	9085	1	2	3	3	4
36	9.9080	9074	9069	9063	9057	9052	9046	9041	9035	9029	1	2	3	3	4
37	9.9023	9018	9012	9006	9000	8995	8989	8983	8977	8971	1	2	3	4	5
38	9.8965	8959	8953	8947	8941	8935	8929	8923	8917	8911	1	2	3	4	5
39	9.8905	8899	8893	8887	8880	8874	8868	8862	8855	8849	1	2	3	4	5
40	9.8843	8836	8830	8823	8817	8810	8804	8797	8791	8784	1	2	3	4	5
41	9.8778	8771	8765	8758	8751	8745	8738	8731	8724	8718	1	2	3	4	5
42	9.8711	8704	8697	8690	8683	8676	8669	8662	8655	8648	1	2	4	5	6
43	9.8641	8634	8627	8620	8613	8606	8598	8591	8584	8577	1	2	4	5	6
44	9.8569	8562	8555	8547	8540	8532	8525	8517	8510	8502	1	2	4	5	6

Numbers in difference columns to be subtracted, not added.
After each function as taken from table is to be written −10.

°	0'	6'	12'	18'	24'	30'	36'	42'	48'	54'	1	2	3	4	5
45	9.8495	8487	8480	8472	8464	8457	8449	8441	8433	8426	1	2	4	5	6
46	9.8418	8410	8402	8394	8386	8378	8370	8362	8354	8346	1	3	4	5	7
47	9.8338	8330	8322	8313	8305	8297	8289	8280	8272	8264	1	3	4	5	7
48	9.8255	8247	8238	8230	8221	8213	8204	8195	8187	8178	1	3	4	5	7
49	9.8169	8161	8152	8143	8134	8125	8117	8108	8099	8090	2	3	5	6	8
50	9.8081	8072	8063	8053	8044	8035	8026	8017	8007	7998	2	3	5	6	8
51	9.7989	7979	7970	7960	7951	7941	7932	7922	7913	7903	2	3	5	7	8
52	9.7893	7884	7874	7864	7854	7844	7835	7825	7815	7805	2	3	5	7	8
53	9.7795	7785	7774	7764	7754	7744	7734	7723	7713	7703	2	3	5	7	8
54	9.7692	7682	7671	7661	7650	7640	7629	7618	7607	7597	2	3	5	7	8
55	9.7586	7575	7564	7553	7542	7531	7520	7509	7498	7487	2	4	5	7	9
56	9.7476	7464	7453	7442	7430	7419	7407	7396	7384	7373	2	4	5	7	9
57	9.7361	7349	7338	7326	7314	7302	7290	7278	7266	7254	2	4	6	8	10
58	9.7242	7230	7218	7205	7193	7181	7168	7156	7143	7131	2	4	6	8	10
59	9.7118	7106	7093	7080	7068	7055	7042	7029	7016	7003	2	4	6	9	11
60	9.6990	6977	6963	6950	6937	6923	6910	6896	6883	6869	2	4	6	9	11
61	9.6856	6842	6828	6814	6801	6787	6773	6759	6744	6730	2	5	7	9	12
62	9.6716	6702	6687	6673	6659	6644	6629	6615	6600	6585	2	5	7	9	12
63	9.6570	6556	6541	6526	6510	6495	6480	6465	6449	6434	3	5	8	10	13
64	9.6418	6403	6387	6371	6356	6340	6324	6308	6292	6276	3	5	8	11	13
65	9.6259	6243	6227	6210	6194	6177	6161	6144	6127	6110	3	5	8	11	13
66	9.6093	6076	6059	6042	6024	6007	5990	5972	5954	5937	3	6	9	11	14
67	9.5919	5901	5883	5865	5847	5828	5810	5792	5773	5754	3	6	9	12	15
68	9.5736	5717	5698	5679	5660	5641	5621	5602	5583	5563	3	6	10	13	16
69	9.5543	5523	5504	5484	5463	5443	5423	5402	5382	5361	3	7	10	14	17
70	9.5341	5320	5299	5278	5256	5235	5213	5192	5170	5148	4	7	11	15	18
71	9.5126	5104	5082	5060	5037	5015	4992	4969	4946	4923	4	8	11	15	19
72	9.4900	4876	4853	4829	4805	4781	4757	4733	4709	4684	4	8	12	16	20
73	9.4659	4634	4609	4584	4559	4533	4508	4482	4456	4430	4	9	13	17	21
74	9.4403	4377	4350	4323	4296	4269	4242	4214	4186	4158	5	9	14	18	22
75	9.4130	4102	4073	4049	4015	3986	3957	3927	3897	3867	5	10	15	19	24
76	9.3837	3806	3775	3745	3713	3682	3650	3618	3586	3554	5	11	16	21	26
77	9.3521	3488	3455	3421	3387	3353	3319	3284	3250	3214	6	11	17	23	28
78	9.3179	3143	3107	3070	3034	2997	2959	2921	2883	2845	6	12	18	25	31
79	9.2806	2767	2727	2687	2647	2606	2565	2524	2482	2439	7	14	20	27	34
80	9.2397	2353	2310	2266	2221	2176	2131	2085	2038	1991	7	15	23	30	38
81	9.1943	1895	1847	1797	1747	1697	1646	1594	1542	1489	8	17	25	33	42
82	9.1436	1381	1326	1271	1214	1157	1099	1040	0981	0920	10	19	29	39	49
83	9.0859	0797	0734	0670	0605	0539	0472	0403	0334	0264	11	22	33	44	55
84	9.0192	0120	0046	9970	9894	9816	9736	9655	9573	9489	13	26	39	52	65
85	8.9403	9315	9226	9135	9041	8946	8849	8749	8647	8543					
86	8.8436	8326	8213	8098	7979	7857	7731	7602	7468	7330	Difference useless				
87	8.7188	7041	6889	6731	6567	6397	6220	6035	5842	5640	due to rapidity of				
88	8.5428	5206	4971	4723	4459	4179	3880	3558	3210	2832	change in log				
89	8.2419	1961	1450	0870	0200	9408	8439	7190	5429	2418	cosine.				

Numbers in difference columns to be subtracted, not added.
After each function as taken from table is to be written −10.

°	0′	6′	12′	18′	24′	30′	36′	42′	48′	54′	1 2 3	4 5
0	−∞	7.242	5429	7190	8439	9408	ō200	ō870	ī450	ī962		
1	8.2419	2833	3211	3559	3881	4181	4461	4725	4973	5208	Difference useless	
2	8.5431	5643	5845	6038	6223	6401	6571	6736	6894	7046	due to rapidity	
3	8.7194	7337	7475	7609	7739	7865	7988	8107	8223	8336	of change in log	
4	8.8446	8554	8659	8762	8862	8960	9056	9150	9241	9331	tangent.	
5	8.9420	9506	9591	9674	9756	9836	9915	9992	ōō68	ō143		
6	9.0216	0289	0360	0430	0499	0567	0633	0699	0764	0828		
7	9.0891	0954	1015	1076	1135	1194	1252	1310	1367	1423	10 20 30	39 49
8	9.1478	1533	1587	1640	1693	1745	1797	1848	1898	1948	9 17 26	35 44
9	9.1997	2046	2094	2142	2189	2236	2282	2328	2374	2419	8 16 24	31 39
10	9.2463	2507	2551	2594	2637	2680	2722	2764	2805	2846	7 14 21	28 35
11	9.2887	2927	2967	3006	3046	3085	3123	3162	3200	3237	7 13 20	26 33
12	9.3275	3312	3349	3385	3422	3458	3493	3529	3564	3599	6 12 18	24 30
13	9.3634	3668	3702	3736	3770	3804	3837	3870	3903	3935	6 11 16	22 28
14	9.3968	4000	4032	4064	4095	4127	4158	4189	4220	4250	5 10 16	21 26
15	9.4281	4311	4341	4371	4400	4430	4459	4488	4517	4546	5 10 15	20 25
16	9.4575	4603	4632	4660	4688	4716	4744	4771	4799	4826	5 9 14	18 23
17	9.4853	4880	4907	4934	4961	4987	5014	5040	5066	5092	4 8 13	17 21
18	9.5118	5143	5169	5195	5220	5245	5270	5295	5320	5345	4 8 13	17 21
19	9.5370	5394	5419	5443	5467	5491	5516	5539	5563	5587	4 8 12	16 20
20	9.5611	5634	5658	5681	5704	5727	5750	5773	5796	5819	4 8 12	15 19
21	9.5842	5864	5887	5909	5932	5954	5976	5998	6020	6042	4 7 11	15 18
22	9.6064	6086	6108	6129	6151	6172	6194	6215	6236	6257	3 7 11	14 18
23	9.6279	6300	6321	6341	6362	6383	6404	6424	6445	6465	3 7 11	14 17
24	9.6486	6506	6527	6547	6567	6587	6607	6627	6647	6667	3 7 10	13 17
25	9.6687	6706	6726	6746	6765	6785	6804	6824	6843	6863	3 7 10	13 16
26	9.6882	6901	6920	6939	6958	6977	6996	7015	7034	7053	3 6 10	13 16
27	9.7072	7090	7109	7128	7146	7165	7183	7202	7220	7238	3 6 9	12 15
28	9.7257	7275	7293	7311	7330	7348	7366	7384	7402	7420	3 6 9	12 15
29	9.7438	7455	7473	7491	7509	7526	7544	7562	7579	7597	3 6 9	12 15
30	9.7614	7632	7649	7667	7684	7701	7719	7736	7753	7771	3 6 9	12 15
31	9.7788	7805	7822	7839	7856	7873	7890	7907	7924	7941	3 6 9	11 14
32	9.7958	7975	7992	8008	8025	8042	8059	8075	8092	8109	3 6 9	11 14
33	9.8125	8142	8158	8175	8191	8208	8224	8241	8257	8274	3 6 9	11 14
34	9.8290	8306	8323	8339	8355	8371	8388	8404	8420	8436	3 5 8	11 13
35	9.8452	8468	8484	8501	8517	8533	8549	8565	8581	8597	3 5 8	11 13
36	9.8613	8629	8644	8660	8676	8692	8708	8724	8740	8755	3 5 8	10 13
37	9.8771	8787	8803	8818	8834	8850	8865	8881	8897	8912	3 5 8	10 13
38	9.8928	8944	8959	8975	8990	9006	9022	9037	9053	9068	3 5 8	10 13
39	9.9084	9099	9115	9130	9146	9161	9176	9192	9207	9223	3 5 8	10 13
40	9.9238	9254	9269	9284	9300	9315	9330	9346	9361	9376	3 5 8	10 13
41	9.9392	9407	9422	9438	9453	9468	9483	9499	9514	9529	3 5 8	10 13
42	9.9544	9560	9575	9590	9605	9621	9636	9651	9666	9681	3 5 8	10 13
43	9.9697	9712	9727	9742	9757	9772	9788	9803	9818	9833	3 5 8	10 13
44	9.9848	9864	9879	9894	9909	9924	9939	9955	9970	9985	3 5 8	10 13

After each function as taken from table is to be written −10.

°	0′	6′	12′	18′	24′	30′	36′	42′	48′	54′	1 2 3	4 5
45	10.0000	0015	0030	0045	0061	0076	0091	0106	0121	0136	3 5 8	10 13
46	10.0152	0167	0182	0197	0212	0228	0243	0258	0273	0288	3 5 8	10 13
47	10.0303	0319	0334	0349	0364	0379	0395	0410	0425	0440	3 5 8	10 13
48	10.0456	0471	0486	0501	0517	0532	0547	0562	0578	0593	3 5 8	10 13
49	10.0608	0624	0639	0654	0670	0685	0700	0716	0731	0746	3 5 8	10 13
50	10.0762	0777	0793	0808	0824	0839	0854	0870	0885	0901	3 5 8	10 13
51	10.0916	0932	0947	0963	0978	0994	1010	1025	1041	1056	3 5 8	10 13
52	10.1072	1088	1103	1119	1135	1150	1166	1181	1197	1213	3 5 8	10 13
53	10.1229	1245	1260	1276	1292	1308	1324	1340	1356	1371	3 5 8	10 13
54	10.1387	1403	1419	1435	1451	1467	1483	1499	1516	1532	3 5 8	10 13
55	10.1548	1564	1580	1596	1612	1629	1645	1661	1677	1694	3 6 9	11 14
56	10.1710	1726	1743	1759	1776	1792	1809	1825	1842	1858	3 6 9	11 14
57	10.1875	1891	1908	1925	1941	1958	1975	1992	2008	2025	3 6 9	11 14
58	10.2042	2059	2076	2093	2110	2127	2144	2161	2178	2195	3 6 9	11 14
59	10.2212	2229	2247	2264	2281	2299	2316	2333	2351	2368	3 6 9	11 14
60	10.2386	2403	2421	2438	2456	2474	2491	2509	2527	2545	3 6 9	12 15
61	10.2562	2580	2598	2616	2634	2652	2670	2689	2707	2725	3 6 9	12 15
62	10.2743	2762	2780	2798	2817	2835	2854	2872	2891	2910	3 6 10	13 16
63	10.2928	2947	2966	2985	3004	3023	3042	3061	3080	3099	3 6 10	13 16
64	10.3118	3137	3157	3176	3196	3215	3235	3254	3274	3294	3 7 10	13 16
65	10.3313	3333	3353	3373	3393	3413	3433	3453	3473	3494	3 7 10	13 16
66	10.3514	3535	3555	3576	3596	3617	3638	3659	3679	3700	3 7 11	14 17
67	10.3721	3743	3764	3785	3806	3828	3849	3871	3892	3914	4 7 11	14 18
68	10.3936	3958	3980	4002	4024	4046	4068	4091	4113	4136	4 7 11	15 18
69	10.4158	4181	4204	4227	4250	4273	4296	4319	4342	4366	4 8 12	15 19
70	10.4389	4413	4437	4461	4485	4509	4533	4557	4581	4606	4 8 12	16 20
71	10.4630	4655	4680	4705	4730	4755	4780	4805	4831	4857	4 8 13	17 21
72	10.4882	4908	4934	4960	4986	5013	5039	5066	5093	5120	4 9 13	18 22
73	10.5147	5174	5201	5229	5256	5284	5312	5340	5368	5397	5 9 14	19 23
74	10.5425	5454	5483	5512	5541	5570	5600	5629	5659	5689	5 10 15	19 24
75	10.5719	5750	5780	5811	5842	5873	5905	5936	5968	6000	5 10 16	21 26
76	10.6032	6065	6097	6130	6163	6196	6230	6264	6298	6332	6 11 17	22 28
77	10.6366	6401	6436	6471	6507	6542	6578	6615	6651	6688	6 12 18	24 30
78	10.6725	6763	6800	6838	6877	6915	6954	6994	7033	7073	6 13 19	26 32
79	10.7113	7154	7195	7236	7278	7320	7363	7406	7449	7493	7 14 21	28 35
80	10.7537	7581	7626	7672	7718	7764	7811	7858	7906	7954	8 15 23	31 38
81	10.8003	8052	8102	8152	8203	8255	8307	8360	8413	8467	9 17 26	34 43
82	10.8522	8577	8633	8690	8748	8806	8865	8924	8985	9046	10 19 29	39 48
83	10.9109	9172	9236	9301	9367	9433	9501	9570	9640	9711	11 22 34	45 56
84	10.9784	9857	9932	0008	0085	0164	0244	0326	0409	0494	13 26 40	53 66
85	11.0580	0669	0759	0850	0944	1040	1138	1238	1341	1446		
86	11.1554	1664	1777	1893	2012	2135	2261	2391	2525	2663	Difference useless	
87	11.2806	2954	3106	3264	3429	3599	3777	3962	4155	4357	due to rapidity	
88	11.4569	4792	5027	5275	5539	5819	6119	6441	6789	7167	of change in log	
89	11.7581	8038	8550	9130	9800	0591	1561	2810	4571	7581	tangent.	

After each function as taken from table is to be written −10.

INDEX